ONE LAST SHOT

For information, write to:
KC&S Publishing,
2999 Fairingford Road,
Westlake Village, CA 91361

e-mail: mzegar@pacbell.net

Design: Heather Hane-Karr
Illustration: Tyler West

Library of Congress Card Number: 98-96682

ONE LAST SHOT

*Mark Levin
is a man with a dream:
to play in the U.S. Amateur golf championship.*

BY MARC ZEGAR

To Lori,

I love you. You're my best friend. You're my only friend.
Thank you for my children.

FOREWORD

Serious players often comment about golf imitating life.

"One Last Shot" is more like a play in which readers choose their parts. We view our golf game much the way we see our life game. We play the same shots in the game as in our daily regimen. We react similarly, as well displaying the same emotions.

This story may help you focus upon what is really important. Then again, I suppose, it depends which part you have chosen to play.

—Marc Zegar

o n e

The breeze through the treetops brought little relief on this warm, hazy day. I felt the perspiration, small heavy droplets pouring off my nose. Should I wipe it off? Should I back away? A million thoughts passed quickly through my mind. Damn it! Where was my father when I wanted him most? I imagined him standing greenside, his arms loosely folded, his right hand at his chin, just as he used to stand admiring a summer evening or having a smoke. Backing away, I mopped up the sweat with my shirtsleeves. As soon as you start to think so much, it's time to regroup, to start your routine all over again. I knew how important this was; I was standing over the last three feet of my round. Luckily, there were no officials around to penalize me for slow play. Taking a deep breath, I surveyed the scene. Two hundred yards behind me, through the warm summer haze, the group behind mine waited patiently for me to putt out. Off to my left, a multitude of cars pressed urgently past on the road beside the golf course.

Finally, I studied my line. The ground beneath my feet seemed heavy and dry; the grass had a shine that suggested stress. I noticed one of the greenkeepers off to the back of the green with a hose waiting to spray the playing surface down. Finally, I exhaled. I was glad I'd be able to putt out before the green would be saturated with water, changing its speed.

Before stepping back over the putt, I shot a glance at my wife, Jane. She was shifting from one foot to the other, putting her hands to her face. Jane had never seemed more lovely to me than at that moment, standing on the side of the green, nervous for me. Even seven months pregnant, she was beautiful: long, lean legs; lithe, gentle curves, like a dancer's; soft chestnut hair falling down over her delicate shoulders. And in her belly, our unborn child, due to arrive in our lives in just a couple of months.

Finally, I approached my putt once again. "Here we go," I said to myself. And immediately, I knew that backing away from the putt had been the right move. Smoothly, slowly, my left hand pushed the putter into the backswing, and I knew there was no turning back.

"Here we go," I thought again, as my left and right hands, sealed together, started the putter head moving forward through the ball. I watched as though someone else was putting as the club struck the ball, a bit thin, but rolling nicely. For a moment, worry and doubt entered my mind. Had I known that all I had to do was put a perfect roll on the ball, I would not have worried. But I knew that perfect putts didn't always go in the hole. The golf gods saw to that.

Finally, I looked up. The ball rolled slowly toward the center of the hole, looked in for what seemed an eternity, and finally fell: the gorgeous, unmistakable sound of the ball settling in the bottom of the cup.

For the first time that day, I smiled brightly. At forty-three years of age, I, Mark Levin, was on my way to my first United States Amateur Championship.

t w o

The phone call came at about 7 p.m. In a matter of minutes, we were in the car heading east, to the desert, to see my dad. On the road we were silent, the only sound the hypnotic hum of the tires on the pavement. For the entire three-hour trip we drove like that, silent, as I sped on, passing startled drivers as quickly as possible, in any lane possible. We must have looked like crash test dummies: no smiles, blank expressions on each ashen face, racing forward in a white Mercedes-Benz.

During the phone call, my aunt had told me that if I wanted to see my father again, I'd better come quickly. He had had a stroke the year before; not much of him was left now. I had to at least try to say goodbye. We had never been close; like many families, mine was a mess, staying together only because we were all familiar with the same brand of misery.

My father had not had a great life. More money had been spent on keeping him alive over the previous year then he had earned in his lifetime. If they had really known him, the government could have saved a lot of money. If they had given him half the money they were spending freely upon him now a few years earlier, he would have given them permission to let him die at the first sign of serious illness. He hated doctors, hospitals and complainers - I think because, secretly, he was scared to death of hospitals, dreaded the thought of dying in such an awful place.

As we drove, I wondered where the sadness I was feeling was coming from. I did not think it had anything directly to do with my father. After all, he was not a man that I could look up to and respect. He wasn't a bad man; I just didn't know him. What I knew about the normal relationship a son has with his father I had gleaned in large part from books, movies and friends. Some men remember, with more than passing fondness, feelings of great support and strength from their fathers; I had no such memories. My father was absent from my life, unavailable to share my dreams and help me find my place in life.

As a result, all my life I have found it hard to feel a sense of belonging, anywhere. Even when I joined one of the most prestigious country clubs in town, after immediate acceptance. That was just about money - not acceptance, respect and friendship.

Looking back, I wished my father had had the capacity to share. Any kind of sharing would have been sufficient. Even among the old, strong-silent-type men at my golf club, I saw the capacity to share - even with sons they considered wayward, with whom they had seemingly never made a connection of any lasting significance. On Father's Day, on the occasional weekend, a truce would be declared, a connection, if only for a brief moment, renewed. I had seen it again and again; a moment or two of healing, reconciliation and consolation - full of immeasurable benefits, good for the soul.

Looking over at Jane, silent in the passenger's seat, I was determined to do it differently: to be more like the younger fathers I'd seen at the club, who were determined to make golf outings with their sons more than a truce. I didn't care that I'd had no real role model, no one to show me properly how to be a father. My child, recently conceived and growing peacefully in my wife's womb, was going to be my "NBF". . . . my new best friend.

The desert sky was bright with a moonlight that lit the expanse of sand and cactus in every direction.

Metal windmills had taken over whole sections of the desert valley and overrun the mountain ridges off in the distance. Finally, we turned off the freeway, a few miles past Palm Springs. The hospital, three or four minutes through town, seemed strangely beautiful, its buildings glowing white in the moonlight. Only a large, flashing red sign -"EMERGENCY ROOM"- convinced me that Jane and I were indeed in the right place.

As we parked, a cloud moved over the moon and it began to rain. Quickly, softly. By the time we were out of the car, it had stopped. I breathed in the humidity, the smell of warm, wet asphalt. A familiar smell - a smell from my childhood, from the New York department store parking lot where my friends and I had played baseball. When it rained, you could see the steam rising from the sun-baked surface. I wondered whether this was the smell I would remember of my father's death.

As we entered the hospital, I remembered the time when my father's sister, my Aunt Rose, told the story of my father's youth. Since my father didn't get along with her - as an adult, he had distanced himself from her and everyone else connected with his childhood - I was lucky to ever hear the story in the first place.

"Your father was a cute boy," she told me, in New York from Pittsburgh for a funeral. "I was in my teens at the time. Very happy, very full of life. Until the pogroms. This was 1915, and your father was five years old. We lived in a small, mostly agricultural village not 30 miles from Warsaw, Poland. We and the rest of the local Jewish peasantry were lined up along both sides of the main road through town. The men were on one side, the women and children on the other. Each group was tethered together by ropes tied to each person's wrists. The crying of the children filled the air. Old men and women groaned and wailed. Everyone could sense that something awful was going to happen.

"It was then that the men on horseback came. Maybe 60 of them. Each rider would pick someone out of the crowd of Jews lining the road, tie his victim's hair to the back of his horse, then drag that poor person up and down the dirt road through town. If the victim was a young woman, then she'd be taken behind a bush and violated. In our place by the roadside, we could hardly see what was happening, the cloud of dust was so thick. But we could hear it, hear the thunderous galloping. Looting and robbing weren't enough. They had to rape and murder.

"Your father was only five when this happened. I was older; I was twelve. Old enough to know that this was not all there was to life. That there was happiness, family, laughter, love. For your father, though, any understanding of this disappeared on that day. He had been told that to be Jewish was to be special. Didn't the family celebrate holidays all year long to rejoice in its good fortune and grace from God? He had been made to feel special - chosen by this God who celebrated with his family. On that day, however, he did not feel special; to him, there was no longer a God."

That day, sitting with Aunt Rose, I finally began to start understanding my father. The long, morose silences. The sudden sighs. The faraway look in his eyes. His inability to make any real connection with the people in his life. If love was destined to be ripped asunder in a pogrom, after all, why love? I saw then that my father's perspective was twisted and perverse, shaped by a nightmare childhood.

But while I had begun to understand my father, I could not forgive him his coldness, could not love him. A father is supposed to give something to his children. The best I got from my father was an example not to follow.

That night as I entered the hospital to see my father for the last time, I promised to teach my unborn child that life is to be played, not just endured or survived.

three

Three nurses came into my father's room, three plain faces without expression or a hint of emotion. One helped restrain and tie down the patient, the second adjusted the wires coming out of the patient's body, and the third washed him like an automobile, carefully soaping all his parts, plying each nook and cranny of his body with the soapy sponge, before efficiently moving along to the next step: rinse and dry operations. This was the miracle of modern medicine.

What remained when the nurses were gone was a man writhing in pain. He was blind as a result of the recent eight-hour operation to save his life - an unexpected complication - and he couldn't speak, was obviously disoriented and generally out of his mind.

I was not going to be able to say goodbye. Damn him! Once again, he had deprived me of the chance to communicate, to connect with him. Here it was - our final opportunity to be truthful with each other without false bravado or posturing - and we could do nothing with it.

Then I looked at my father, really studied him. Eyes closed against the pain; struggling to breathe steadily. His small body tinier than ever as he approached death. The body of a five-year-old boy. And I realized: His life was a quiet voice on a windy day, overwhelmed by the elements. I couldn't speak; and for the first time in my life I couldn't pretend that I didn't love him. I didn't even really know him, but I loved him. He was my father.

As I studied my father, I had a vision of him standing in the corner of the hospital room, his arms folded in his customary fashion. I remembered those times when I was a small child and my father had been banned from the house. There he would stand, arms crossed, cigarette in hand, looking for long periods of time up at the sky.

Looking back to the frail body in the hospital bed, I thought through what I knew about him and his life. He was wiry, about 5' 7" and most of 130 pounds, with long, wavy, grayish-brown hair, even late in life. I never saw him exercise, but he had great vitality and had never missed a day's work that I knew of. He had large ears and a large Jewish nose. On the whole, he looked like the stereotypical Jewish tailor.

He wasn't a tailor. Close enough, though - he was a haberdasher. I remembered the way he would gently caress the fabric of a man's sport coat or shirt - efficiently, and without embarrassment, but with care. As I became more successful and wore more expensive clothes, he often did the same to me, as if to judge my success by the weight of the wool in my suit or the softness of the silk in my shirt. And as I grew older, I realized that I like to feel fabrics myself. So he did give me something.

Women loved his eyes, or so I had been told. A soft, sky blue, they seemed the eyes of a sensitive man, someone you could confide in. If only he had had more time to rid himself of his anger, perhaps he could have become the man those eyes were made for. In life, as in golf, anger and rage serve no one well.

I wondered if he had indeed mellowed in his old age, if that was yet another secret he had kept from me. I knew that, in recent years, most who knew him said he had a sweet smile and kind disposition. Of course, they had never experienced the sullen silences, the explosive, violent outbursts, of my childhood, his early manhood. I wanted to ask him, finally, what he was thinking or feeling. But for some reason I could not.

I looked back over to the corner of the hospital room. My father was still there, looking at me, nodding his approval. He smiled softly and made a thumbs-up gesture. It was what I had always wanted: approval from my father.

However, I will never really know if it was me or the nursing crew he approved of that day.

four

A feeling of excitement, something akin to electricity, coursed through my body as I took my seat in Coach. The seat was ridiculously small, causing my knees to press hard against the seat in front of me. My God! I thought. I'm only 5'9". What do guys over six feet tall do? This was just great. There'd be no way I'd be able to relax. And I needed to relax before this, the biggest tournament of my life.

With a major effort, I managed to close my eyes and drift into a daydream. Immediately, I saw myself as the skinny little 14-year-old kid who used to hang around the Rancho Park driving range. I don't know why, but I think about those years a lot lately.

Rancho Park was sort of a public, Jewish country club, if such a place is possible. Young executives and professionals from Cheviot Hills came to Rancho to call upon the services of my colleagues and myself. Supposedly, most of them were waiting for an opening at one of the two Jewish clubs on the Westside. Maybe they were. They certainly weren't waiting for an invitation from one of the three gentile clubs. This was, and is, a fact of golfing life in Los Angeles.

I thought of myself as pretty independent at 14. I came and went as I pleased at home, and generally fended for myself. I showed up at school on a regular basis, doing pretty well there. But because of my father, there wasn't a whole lot for me at home. Still, somehow, I was expected to become a doctor or lawyer. To do that, I knew I would need money for college. That's what first drew me to the golf course: the chance to make some cash.

My introduction to caddying came from the Caddie Master. Pat Lott was a big, black man ("colored," in those days) who always had a cigar in his mouth. For some reason, he took to me and loved me. He must have liked the way I took nothing for granted, but instead showed up at 5:00 a.m. everyday, ahead of the ghetto boys, in the hopes of getting a loop.

I was the only white boy who caddied regularly at Rancho, on the weekends during the school year and full time during the summer. The other white boys caddied for their dads or their dads' friends. And there weren't many of those.

Make money I did. And usually - when I was getting regular loops, that is - I didn't even have to spend money on food. When you got out early, most of the time you didn't have to spend your hard-earned cash on food at the course restaurant; you could generally depend on your man (no women golfers I knew of at Rancho Park took a caddie) to buy you something to eat and drink at the 12th hole. Usually, it was a hot dog and lemonade. I would start tasting them at about the ninth green. A caddie carrying 40-50 pounds on each shoulder could start hallucinating going up the steep grade of the 10th hole, thinking about that hot dog and lemonade.

Business was brisk at Rancho. But I had to work like a dog for my money. It was not unusual for me to walk 36 or even 45 holes carrying two bags. In those days, the bags' straps were leather and sometimes less than two inches wide, and they would hurt. One bag I carried had its brand name on the strap, and left an impression of that logo on my shoulder for a week!

Money may have been the first thing to draw me to the golf course, but soon I found a number of other reasons to love Rancho Park. For one thing, at Rancho I got the sense of community I was lacking at home. The caddie shack became my home away from home.

The caddie shack wasn't really a shack. It was more of a chainlink corral with a few benches and old folding chairs scattered about a picnic table, which was always occupied by at least two card players - even late in the afternoon, after the chance of looping had come and gone. Cigar and cigarette smoke wafted through the air, hanging on clouds of beer breath. The older caddies all had regular spots in the shade. Kids, however, didn't have regular spots. We just sort of hunkered down anywhere, eavesdropping on sexy stories, off-color jokes and talk of touring pros and how they paid their caddies after this win or that finish.

My first few months at Rancho also introduced me to the game of golf. After my first week, I purchased my first putter (a brand new "Bullseye") for about $8. This was handy because, if I didn't get a loop, I could putt for quarters with the rich kids who didn't work and got something called an allowance. I thought they were rich, but then again any kid with money in his pocket that he didn't have to caddie for was rich as far as I was concerned. Their allowances were my bounty, and I hunted that bounty with fervor and passion.

When they weren't around, there were caddies to putt with, but they hunted guys like me in the same way I hunted rich kids. Sometimes I would just hang around and watch the Rancho regulars - a group of older, white men who would occupy the practice putting green much of the day. There were Fast Eddy, Ed, Big Ed, Rooster, Schwartz, all betting quarters, halves and sometimes dollars.

Other times, I would head over to the driving range, where Jetson Mitchell, a black man in his twenties who worked the range until closing, would give me informal lessons. Jetson Mitchell was a truly impressive golfer; even today, I wonder what kind of career he would have had, had he been white. He looked like the sleekest Ferrari swinging at the ball. He was 150 pounds, 5'11" tall, and had ebony-black skin that appeared painted over muscles so long and taut they seemed like strands of steel cable. I could lift weights all day and never have his body. It came from the kind of life lived in the South Central Los Angeles ghetto, from a brand of labor most white folks could not conceive of nor abide.

Jetson's move through the ball was athletic, served up on a flat plane from what seemed miles from the ball. He reached for the ball at impact, getting completely extended. Again and again, he would send 60 compression range balls out of the driving range. Players on the ninth tee, on the other side of the fence 320 yards away, were in jeopardy. Never before nor since, have I seen anyone drive the ball so far. But that wasn't the half of it. He had an efficient short game, and got tremendous height on 1 and 2 irons. While he was subject to bouts of wildness, this was more immaturity than lack of skill. Needless to say, he didn't get any scholarships to Arizona State, never had proper guidance, role models or coaching.

I loved Jetson. He gave me range balls to beat, and I helped him pick those and others up at closing. He gave me a place to go, the sense of family I sorely needed.

Jetson's friend OB was the one who really taught me how to swing, though. We started with a wedge and worked our way down to long irons over a period of six months. I hit thousands of balls with each club before graduating to the next. Along the way, I acquired a Marilyn Smith driver and an old Wilson 4 wood. OB didn't teach me how to hit those, but somehow I figured them out on my own.

I beat thousands of balls for six months before I ever played the hallowed grounds of Rancho Park. And then came my first real round (actually, nine holes). I played with OB, Jetson and the local Jewish hopeful (a Cheviot Hills brat who went into business with his father after college, never to be heard from again as far as competitive golf was concerned), and shot 42. Before the round, the guys had me paranoid about slashing it around and holding up play. As a result, I had first-tee jitters on every hole; I thought the entire golf course was watching me. But I realized very soon that, outside of our foursome, most everyone slashed it around. That's why it took five hours or more to play at Rancho Park.

five

Damn! I thought. My knee was killing me. I wasn't sure why. I hadn't banged or wrenched it; it just hurt. And stuck as I was in too-small a plane seat, there wasn't much I could do about it. Whoever said only women have biological clocks? There I was, 43 years, still hoping to compete with kids half my age. In a strange way, I looked forward to turning 50; the shorter courses do have their attraction.

Two hours and 43 more minutes before arrival. Jane hadn't been able to come, even though now I needed her more than ever. She had always caddied for me in the big events, and I knew it wouldn't be the same without her. She deserved to be there, too, after all the lousy qualifying rounds she had had to suffer through. She was eight and a halfmonths pregnant, though.

The truth is I felt guilty about leaving her. But I had tried to qualify for the U.S. Amateur and U.S. Mid-Amateur at least eight times each, and had come close, but always missed. There was no way I wasn't going to be there, now that I'd qualified for the U.S. Amateur Championship.

Poor Jane. I had warned her, though. I had made the mistake of not warning my first wife, but Jane I had warned. I had warned her that I wasn't going to play the rich, Jewish lawyer anymore. That I was trying to devote myself to the game I loved: golf. Try as I might, I could not scare her off. Not only did she love me, she was my best and most understanding friend.

Before making the momentous decision to devote myself to golf, I had spent ten years of my life in the ring of corporate litigation. I was a litigator. I represented banks, S & Ls and title insurance companies.

And I always won. After all, I was supposed to win. My opponents were deadbeats who refused to pay my clients what they were due, or so I thought.

My passion (anger?) served me well. I was consumed with truth, justice and foreclosure. Opposing counsel got the message that my office would work through the night, if need be, to be ready to fight in the morning over a few thousand dollars. This kind of energy (anger?) frightened most opposing counsel; they generally caved in.

I made millions of dollars while riding on the backs of young associates I hired to do the grunt work. The harder they worked, the more money I made, and the more they wanted to be like me. They never understood: The one who gets the clients (at least those who pay within 30 days) makes all the money.

I considered myself lucky to have made it as a lawyer. After all, I had come from relative poverty. And then I had taken what might best be called a circuitous route to membership in the Bar.

For one thing, I started my studies at Ralph's School of Law. That wasn't the institution's actual name; it was a nickname that came from the school's location: the basement of Ralph's supermarket in West Los Angeles. Ralph's was an unaccredited law school - a school that would take in anyone to get student loan or government program money.

Then there was the fact that I flunked out of Ralph's. This was not an academic flunking; let us just say it was an inability to communicate with the school's dean. In any case, I had nights off after that.

After Ralph's, I continued my studies via a correspondence course. And then, after two years of the correspondence course, I petitioned the California Supreme Court to let me take the bar. They granted my petition.

I failed my first Bar. You couldn't bullshit the Bar examiners. It was their game, and they made the rules....sometimes as they went.

So, I took the Bar exam again. And played it their way.... mindlessly. This time it was their turn to screw up; I passed. I was sworn in on Friday the 13th, July 1979.

Lawyering had ended up treating me well, financially speaking. Sitting there on the plane, my knee screaming in pain, I considered my situation. I had a big house with a big mortgage, but no other debt. I had almost a million dollars in savings, and a 15-unit apartment building that was free and clear. I had a respected place in the community. The only thing lawyering hadn't given me was a great golf game. And that's the one thing I had wanted more than anything since my childhood days at Rancho Park - a chance to master the game that helped me escape home and my father and start making my place in the world. That's why I had - finally - quit lawyering.

Yes, I felt somewhat guilty at having made that decision. After all, I had been brought up to think that work was the only worthwhile thing in the world. Not fun. Not happiness. Not even love. Just work. Only with Jane's help was I able to slow down and realize that it was the time for me to enjoy my life and do what I wanted to do.

I thought about the Senior V.P. for the big automobile company, who, after the golf tournament, handed the winner the oversized check for zillions. More than anything, that executive probably wished he could break 80. Breaking 70 is what I wanted to do. It wasn't important to break 70.... but it was important to me.

Then I thought about two old schoolmates of mine. I used to beat them most of the time, but now they were professionals. They weren't tearing up the PGA Tour, but they were pursuing their dream. They looked good on TV: clean clothes and large tour bags. I never counted their money, but their lives seemed filled with passion (anger?). I wondered: If I had worked as hard at my golf game as I had at lawyering, would I have made the grade?

Just then, the seatbelt light came on. I was on my way to the U.S. Amateur Championship. I was about to learn the answer to my question.

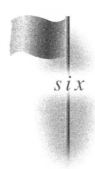

six

My golf game really took off when I left Rancho Park and started caddying at the Bentwood Country Club. Bentwood was a good place to work. The members loved me - especially the women, most of whom were petrified of the young, black caddies and grossed out by the smelly, old white ones. (In those days only a handful of caddies were Hispanic, but these women would not have cared for them, either; they would not have been of their own.) At least half the caddies there were colorful, clean characters. I enjoyed going out on the course with these guys, even if it did mean a lot of extra work.

And then, there was Danny, who ran the food concession. Danny was a good guy. He fed caddies when they were broke, and gave everyone a third chance. He knew how hard life could be. Every day, he wore the same outfit: white pants and a white T-shirt, stretched thinly over his bulging belly and polka-dotted with ketchup and grease stains. Ketchup and grease were, after all, key ingredients of almost every dish he knew how to make.

The only thing I didn't like about Bentwood was the Caddie Master, a man named Bill. He looked like a drill sergeant, somewhat stout with a crew cut, and always had a cigarette in his mouth and a cup of coffee in his hand. His fingers were stained from the smokes. The white shirts he usually wore were clean and neatly pressed, and contrasted with his yellowish eyes and fingers. Both his looks and his demeanor - Bill was mean-spirited and very moody - made me certain he was a drunk.

I made as much as $150 a week in 1967 - more than my father was making, even. But because of Bill's cruelty, I often had to wait around for no reason to get my money. After my loops, I didn't get paid until he cashed me out. Some days, even if I had finished 36 holes by 2 or 3 p.m. - he would refuse to cash me out until 5 p.m. If on one day I tried to leave early, on the next he would make me sit on the bench until 1 or 2 p.m. before giving me a loop with a stiff (Bentwood had plenty of stiffs, one of them being a very famous comedian), or a single nine-hole loop. It would be 10 or 12 hours of sitting around, two hours of actual, paying work.

And then there were the times Bill would use us caddies as slave labor, giving us jobs to do relating to bags we were not handling. For example, taking them to the driving range or to the parking lot - without the possibility of a tip or compensation. Members took these services for granted, not realizing how unfair they were. Caddies were independent contractors, only getting paid when they looped. But if you didn't cooperate with Bill, you were down the road. I can remember guest days when I carried bags to the parking lot and driving range all day long, and then didn't even get a single nine-hole loop.

As I said, though, despite all this, I enjoyed my time at Bentwood. I played a lot of golf, on a very nicely designed and well-kept golf course. I learned games of chance from members and caddies alike. Very soon, I was an accomplished player, playing to a 1 or 2 handicap. Kids these days can be plus 2s by the time they play golf as teenagers, but in 1967, there were not many plus-handicap players playing high school golf. I was a force to be reckoned with in 1967.

I never gambled for a lot of money at Bentwood, but didn't mind wagers placed upon me. I looked forward to playing on Mondays - the day we caddies could get on the course - the way kids look forward to Christmas. I was the center of attention for the first time in my life. Everyone wanted to be my friend. Handicappers would interview me:

"Ya drawin' it or playin' the fade?" one might ask. "How's that back of yours?" another would shout.

Those were exciting times. There might be 20 or 30 caddies following along as I went *mano-a-mano* with my opponent, rooting one or the other of us on. The total pot might be $200 to $300, a veritable fortune to the likes of me. But what I remember more than anything was those times I lost: when I failed my buddies, and they lost their hard-earned cash. I took that very personally.

"Calm down, Mark," my closest pal once told me. "Don't worry about us. Remember, in the end, you're playing for yourself and no one else."

It was a lesson I think I'm still trying to learn. I know I hadn't learned it when, later in life, a successful lawyer, I joined Bentwood as a member. During the 10 years I was a member, I was more concerned with fitting in, with impressing my peers - guys born to wealth, to whom I referred collectively as "the lucky sperm club" - than with just enjoying the game for what it was.

During that time as a member of Bentwood, I never once won the club championship. Again and again, I'd shoot an 80 to take myself out of contention, against guys I'd beaten repeatedly on the weekends. It seemed that what I wanted most would always be beyond my reach in golf. "It's just a game, for Christ's sake," I would tell myself over and over again. But in time, the game began to teach me lessons. Like I had really wanted to win for the wrong reasons. To be accepted. To belong. For them, instead of for me. Eventually, I knew that, when I didn't care about "them," I would finally "get it".....and maybe win for me.

seven

On Saturday morning, I woke up in my Ohio hotel room after a fitful sleep. Outside, the weather was sunny and calm: perfect golf weather. The U.S. Amateur tournament would begin on Monday, but I would be allowed a practice round at each of the two courses to be used in the qualifying rounds early in the week: famous Schofield Village and its lesser-known neighbor, Marborann Country Club.

I would have to play well at Marborann. There was no sense in concentrating solely on Schofield, because all qualifiers for the final rounds would have to play one round at Marborann. In fact, one of my options was to focus on Marborann, to try to shoot lights out to give myself a cushion at Schofield. The way I saw it, a 70 at Marborann would allow a 74, 75 or maybe even a 76 at

Schofield to squeeze by into match play. I hated thinking this way, but I've always been a survivor, a grinder, and it's a mentality that's hard to shake.

I decided I would play Marborann on Saturday, Schofield Village on Sunday. On the way to the course on Saturday, I thought about how crazy it was that I was even here. Was it normal for a grown man to give up his chosen career to chase a dream like this? I thought about all I'd gone through to get where I was.

Why had I put myself in this uncomfortable position? I had worked on my game as though on a mission from the planet Gorgon. I had given up material benefits, such as first class on the airbus, to play a game that humiliates, depresses and confuses everyone who plays it, especially me. Why? And what about the shame and embarrassment that would result if I did any of a thousand things I could do to

look silly or ridiculous on national TV?

Then I thought about some of the great PGA Tour players. Did they feel like they were ready to vomit at the thought of shooting 80 on national TV? By the time I got to the course, I was having an anxiety attack. I needed this like I needed another finger on my hand. But at the driving range, I began to relax. I was hitting the ball well. And I'd always found that when I hit the ball well, I didn't need to know the golf course quite so well. It was hard to shoot over par if you were hitting all the fairways and greens.

I hit it well during my first practice round and left the course feeling really confident, having carded a 73. I hadn't putted everything out, but I was satisfied that I could make the putts when I needed them. Not a smart way to think, but I wasn't going to destroy my newly relaxed state by questioning what had gotten me relaxed in the first place.

At Marborann, I saw, you had to drive the ball solidly, lag putts over 15 feet to tap-in range, and stay away from 6s and 7s. It would be hard to maintain one's confidence after making a 6 or 7 on a supposedly easier course. I would only have two rounds to qualify for the medal rounds, and the thought of having to make another two or three more birdies in addition to the ones I'd already been hoping for in the normal course of my round was a depressing one. Yes, I would have to stay away from 6s and 7s if I was to have any chance at all.

eight

Arriving at Schofield Village the next day was the highlight of my golfing life to that point. Not because of the spotless locker room or the fancy dining room. I had been in plenty of first-class clubhouses, changed my shoes and had coffee in them, and not one had changed my life. This golf course was ranked in a widely circulated golf magazine's top 25, but that stuff was always political; I knew not to be impressed by that nonsense. There are great golf courses that never make that list and are no worse off because of it.

No, this place was great because of the feeling it gave me. Being there, I felt special: I was being allowed to compete in the U.S. Amateur. There was no other place on the planet I would rather have been. It was a dream come true. No one could have felt better about life than I did that morning.

When they designed and built Schofield Village, practice facilities were not an afterthought. More acreage at Schofield Village was devoted to the range and pitching areas then to most nine-hole executive courses. Someone had decided that important missionary work was going to take place at these practice facilities, and they wanted to be sure the natives got the message. No expense was spared-right down to the balata practice balls. And this native got the message.

I practiced hard and long on my putting all Sunday morning. I had my chalkline out on the practice putting green; I felt self-conscious about discoloring the otherwise perfect greens, but I needed my chalkline. Like a bricklayer, I used the chalkline to lay down a perfectly straight line.

First, I'd attach the string to the center of the hole, then pull it tightly about 10 feet away. When I then snapped the chalked string, a crisp, cobalt-blue line would appear on the emerald green grass. I had to find a straight putt to do this, one without any break, or it would do more harm than good. I had to know if my shoulders, hips and feet were aligned properly. I guess they were; my putting felt solid. Each putt I holed was reassurance that I could do it again on command. First five in a row, then ten, from 5 feet. Then back to about 8 feet, where I kept sinking putts. I felt like I could do this forever. I wanted to do this forever. I was piloting my missile. I was in control.

Then, in the afternoon, I played my practice round at Schofield Village. I was paired with three other players, all of whom knew each other from a college tournament in which they had played. One of the players, apparently, was a collegiate star. He had won two tournaments that year and was the number one player at a school ranked in the top five in the nation. He had one of the best scoring averages in collegiate golf and was heralded as a player you would hear about on the PGA Tour. But I quickly realized I should not be in awe of him. On the putting green, he had been fascinated by my chalkline. And through our practice round, I out-drove him regularly. Both mentally and physically, I realized at one point, I belonged here. I belonged at the U.S. Amateur Championship.

But that feeling didn't last long. I didn't score well during this practice round. After six or seven holes, it became apparent I was not going to break par, and maybe not break 80. I didn't want to put any more pressure of myself than was absolutely necessary. I told myself I was just trying to get acquainted with Schofield Village's personality. Unfortunately, that personality turned out to be a surly one. You might hit a slightly errant tee shot and have literally no play from your lie. The golf course was exhausting.

By the end of the round, my chest was tight, my breathing shallow. I was a mess. I found a quiet spot and did some stretching and deep breathing. It helped, but I still left the course feeling as if I had forgotten something: the feeling that I belonged on the golf course. And the next day, of course, everyone would know whether I belonged or not.

Who needs this crap? I asked myself. Why do I do this to myself? Why can't I just play $5 Nassaus at the club, and leave it at that? Why chance shame and embarrassment? Did Ben Hogan think about shame and embarrassment?

This is just a game, right?

nine

Back at the hotel, my sense of dread deepened. Golf is a game, right? And games are fun, right? But right now, "fun" was about as different as possible from what I was experiencing.

So I called Jane. We talked for 15 minutes. She knew how scared I was, even though all we talked about was the weather, my accommodations, things like that. She had felt my dread - she always could - and was now just as scared as I. She loved me that much.

After hanging up, I had a scotch (they say Bobby Jones would have a couple of scotches to get to sleep), then tried to get some sleep. The next day, I thought, I would find some young kid to carry my bag, but I would take full responsibility for all yardage estimates and reads on the greens. I would go quietly through the round, trying to make the experience last as long as I could, since I might never get here again. I would think of Jane, and remember how much she loves me.

These thoughts and others like them ended up lasting through most of the night. If I slept 10 minutes, I was lucky. One part of my conversation with Jane in particular kept running through my mind. In it, I whined self-deprecatingly to her: Here I was, thousands of miles away from her, just as she's about to deliver our first child, spending money we really could use elsewhere, whining about my putting stroke or some such nonsense. Jane, bless her, told me not to worry. Can you imagine - her telling me not to worry, just as she was getting ready to have a baby in a few days?

Your concentration can wander when you're 43. When you don't sleep all night, it definitely wanders. Ironically, difficult trials involving millions of dollars didn't keep me awake three minutes at night - but now, thoughts of rolling a ball into a hole in the ground most certainly did. Climbing out of bed at 6 in the morning, I found myself completely wired. "All you're going to have to do," I told myself, thinking of that day's round, "is concentrate for a minute or two at a time."

Bored, or worried, I called Jane. It was 3 a.m. in California, but she wasn't mad at all. She wouldn't admit it, but she would have been mad if I had wanted to talk at this ungodly hour and didn't call. And I knew she liked to know I was thinking about her at 3 in the morning. After all, a thousand miles away at 3 in the morning, a man could be thinking or doing some really naughty things. "Have fun," she said, as we signed off. "Remember what got you there in the first place."

What a woman! What a wife!

My tee time was 7:28 a.m. at Schofield Village. Early, but okay with me, since the greens would be almost perfect at that time. Besides, I was up and ready to go. I was glad to play there first and get the toughest course out of the way for the two-round qualifying.

It was a beautiful summer morning, and the course was humming. Everything seemed so organized, right down to the balata range balls piled in a pyramid at each driving range position. The media was there; parents were there; college coaches and hundreds of other spectators were there, ready to walk the course. A special feeling - an electricity - filled the air. Being in this event was very special indeed - because each of the guys who were playing had faced at least one putt, like the one I had had, to qualify, and like me, each had made it.

My caddie was 14 years old and cute as hell. You had to be cute to have a name like hers: Michal, or Mike for short. A short girl with short dark hair, she possessed a toothy smile always ready to light up her freckled face. Fortunately for her, my bag was extremely light. Besides the 14 clubs, there were four or five balls and some tees in the small front pocket, a sweatshirt in the long zippered compartment, Bufferin, eye drops and a few ball markers in yet another.

A strange feeling overtook me when I first arrived at the golf course. Suddenly, I was part of this special group of guys: participants in the U.S. Amateur Championship. But I didn't feel at all special. Not like I used to when I entered the courtroom, for example. In that circumstance, I felt powerful, armed with the facts and a $1000 designer suit. Here, though, I felt diminutive.

That feeling intensified as I hit range balls. I felt so detached from everyone and everything, including my caddie. Even Jane was missing from my mind. Hot flashes and thoughts of 80 began to strangle me. "What if this or that happens?" I asked myself. This or that has happened before, I reminded myself. I tried to shake it off, to tell myself that shooting 80 wouldn't kill me, after all. I had made it to the United States Amateur, whatever happened.

They called my name; I was third up. My playing companions were half my age, but bigger and stronger than I am. That's not saying much, though; most every college player these days seems bigger and stronger than me. The boys gave Mike some very noticeable attention. I wished each player luck and apologized to my caddie in advance for any childish behavior that might overcome me.

The first two players hit big drives that found the rough. I immediately remembered playing a match with a former pro in the first round of the Trans-Miss a few years back, a guy who hit it unbelievably long. That year, I qualified for match play, and did well there. The secret at that time was not watching this guy swing or noticing the whereabouts of his ball. He routinely outdrove me by 30 to 50 yards, and it could have been demoralizing watching each ball he hit go into orbit. By tuning him out, I beat him in a playoff - on a par 5, no less.

"On the tee, from Arizona State, former Southwestern Amateur Champion and all American, Steve Bergen. Hit away, please."

Whack!

"On the tee, from South Oak Country Club, Marc Levin." The announcer paused, looking for something else to say. "From South Oak Country Club, Mark Levin," he said again, finally. "Hit away, please."

I walked over to the teeing area. As I bent down to put the tee in the ground, I dropped the ball from my very sweaty hand. My stomach was making audible sounds, and my shirt was beginning to get wet in several places. I could feel the perspiration running down my forehead. As I reached for the ball, the head of my driver hit it, and it rolled across the tee box toward the gallery. I lunged forward to stop the ball, but lost my footing; down I went. In the gallery, everyone started laughing hysterically. Grimacing, I picked myself up off the ground. By this time my hands were shaking badly, and my chest pounding. I could feel large droplets of perspiration running down my body, under my shirt and pants.

After successfully re-teeing the ball, I dried my hands and face with a clean towel. Then I looked out at my shot. The first hole was 446 yards, with a slight dogleg right, from an elevated tee. Bunkers on the right at the elbow and a creek down the left side made it a good opening hole; this golf course demanded your attention in hurry. I tried to stay loose as I took my driver back, concentrating on staying behind the ball at impact.

I necked it dead straight. That's usually how I miss my drives, short and straight. But the elevation of the tee, combined with the hard, fast fairway, helped my drive considerably. Tournament conditions came to my aid, in this case. Normally, amateurs play slower golf courses, whose fairways and greens are not cut as close as on tournament courses. Tournament conditions are stressful to a golf course: Too much traffic on them can mean the loss of greens or even fairways. But this was the U.S. Amateur; Schofield Village was set up as hard and fast as any pro venue.

When I got out onto the fairway, I found I had 193 yards to the front of the green. I couldn't skenk this one and get away with it, because there were four bunkers surrounding the green, but I saw a small opening in front that would allow me to roll it on if necessary. The pin was back and the green was huge. Pulling out my 3 iron, I aimed for the center of the green.

My backswing was a little short, but at least I didn't grab at it on the way down. I hit a low, driving shot that drew toward the front center of the green. After taking one hop 15 feet from the front apron, it rolled to the back edge like a hockey puck on a slick rink. So much for high, soft long irons.

There I was, facing a 30-foot putt on a green that was obviously lightning fast. Are you having fun yet? I asked myself.

Relax, I told myself. After all, I had been putting well for the past two years. If the greens were smooth, I could roll it with the best of them. Putting was probably the best part of my game, after the driver. I was a damn good wedge player, as well. It seemed my mistakes came from stupidity - from not thinking of the percentages when facing a critical shot. There I was, a strategic genius in complex, multi-party litigation - and yet a moron on the golf course. It all makes sense!

The putt was mostly straight, and I almost made it. But when it was done, I found myself facing a 4½ footer coming back. I thought: This could be my tournament, right here. The first hole, and already I was crushing myself with pressure. I noticed that I was still holding my breath as the ball fell in the cup on my second putt. A huge sigh of relief, then onto the next torture chamber.

On the next tee, I hit first; both my playing partners had taken bogey on our first hole of the U.S. Amateur. Suddenly, I began thinking that I really belonged at Schofield Village.

The second hole was 452 yards long, maybe slightly downhill, and looked every inch that length. I would have to keep it right off the tee, because otherwise trees would block my second shot to the green. I hit a good drive and was left with 185 yards. Then I hit a 4 iron to the center of the green. Boy, was I pumped. I can do this, I thought. I can do this. But I sure wished Jane were there.

My caddie was extremely professional in all respects. She never got too excited; she expected me to hit good shots. She knew where to stand and what to do. But I noticed she never looked me square in the eye. I wanted to make a connection with her, but she, on the other hand, did not seem to want to get involved in the outcome of my tournament. Maybe she thought it would put more pressure on me. I wondered if, years from now, she would remember this tournament, this day or even me.

I parred the first six holes, birdied the par-5 seventh, then immediately gave it back on the par 3 eighth with a bogey. Why do I do that? I thought. It must have been really uncomfortable for me to be under par, because I always seemed to give it back when I was.

Still, I realized I had a good rhythm going as I walked up to the ninth tee. The ninth hole was a 410-yard par 4. I had not parred this hole in my practice round, but on this day I felt like a completely different player. A good player, one who gets and deserves the breaks. But, of course, this thought ended up being hubris.

The drive was critical on this hole. Too far to the right, and the trees blocked your shot to the green. Too far to the left, and you're standing on the side of a hill, eye level with the head of your club - if your ball didn't keep rolling into the woods.

I hit it absolutely perfectly given my level of fear. Right on the neck, but straight and, of course, short. Out on the fairway, I eyed the green. It was tilted to the right, framed by a lake and a creek, and had trees almost everywhere around it except off one side of the green. In the center of the green, there was a huge, sloping hump; looking back on it, I am certain at least one elephant is buried under that green. I'm supposed to be a smart guy, but I really couldn't figure out where to hit my shot and give myself even the slightest margin for error. Of course, in the water you make at least 6; I knew at least not to go there.

I decided to hit a 3 iron, because a weak shot in front or to the right would be wet. It was a lot of club, but the pin was back, and anywhere on the green would be that much closer to par. I didn't need to hit it hard, but I did need to hit it. Low, left and hot was too ugly to think about. I just had to stop thinking, period, and zen the ball onto the green.

But when I swung, I was so loosey-goosey that I pulled across the ball and hit a pop fly to right field with an open face. And, sure enough, the shot ended up in the water hazard.

For the first time, Mikey looked right at me. I couldn't believe it; she had finally made some connection with me. She cared, after all. Which was nice to know, because immediately after hitting that adorable shot, I heated up and started to perspire; it felt like a thousand ants were crawling around the top of my head. My hands got very wet, and a cool chill caught me off guard. Seeing my distress, Mikey calmly took another ball from my bag, marked it with a red pen, and handed it to me. She was taking care of me at my time of need. It seemed an endless walk to my next shot, but I needed some time to think, because I was so nervous. After consulting with a course official about where I could take my drop, I settled on a spot 45 yards from the flag.

I hit my pitch shot low and watched it two-hop and then roll right up to the hole....and keep rolling. It wasn't going fast, but it did keep going. I hated it when the golf gods teased me like that. Finally, the ball stopped, 6 feet from the hole.

My next shot would be the difference between "Mo" and "No Mo" (momentum and no momen-

tum). Make it for bogey and save myself from the downward spiral to oblivion, or start the back side two down to Old Man Par. I told myself that it was only one shot; that in the scheme of things, it didn't matter. I just had to qualify, not be low medalist. That thought in mind, I promptly stroked that puppy directly at the center of the hole. The Mo was mine!

Or so it seemed. Instead of falling, my bogey 5 rolled around the lip, then dribbled several inches away from the cup. Double bogey! In my mind, I immediately doubled my front nine score of 38. I decided 76 wasn't the end of the world, but it would put pressure on tomorrow's round I didn't want. I would try to keep it at even par for the back nine, as if I had any choice.

But, of course, the bad luck at number nine was immediately followed by a three-putt bogey at ten. Boy, did that piss me off! I tried like hell not to think about it, though. I didn't want to think myself onto a bogey train I wouldn't be able to get off until three or four bogeys later. All I wanted to think about was my next shot - more difficult than it sounds, of course. But I just had to stop the bleeding.

Steadying myself, I started to feel strong, started playing crisply. I parred the par five 11th hole without much difficulty, then birdied the 12th hole, a par 3 lookalike of the Augusta National 12th. No bridge or anything like that, but everything else about the hole was more than just coincidence.

I had to be careful not to bogey the next hole. It would take all the concentration I had not to give it back after working so hard for the birdie on the previous one. The 13th hole was a long par 4, dogleg left; 442 yards, but fortunately downhill. I smoked one down the right side with a gentle draw. I hit it with little effort, dead solid. For once, I was in control of my missile. At times like that I felt like an astronaut in orbit gliding through the golf zone. But I knew I had to slow down and control the energy coursing through my body, or disaster would likely strike. I had to stay confident, but at the same time stay alert, and not allow myself to get too cocky.

I had 180 yards to the flag, with bunkers on both sides of a long, narrow green. I skenked it dead straight, carrying only about 150 yards or so, ending up on the front edge of the green. Not my best shot, but I've hit great shots that ended up a lot worse. This one would do just fine.

The putt was about 40 feet, slightly downhill but not too squirrelly. It was hard to read, though, because the first 15 feet broke two ways and the last 10 feet seemed to bank left. It also looked slicker than pig snot, and I was feeling a bit timid about the situation. What the hell; I decided to hit it straight and hope for good speed and not just a little luck. I hit it so softly I almost dropped the putter; I had a little deceleration going for me on that one. The ball seemed to be dying before it got even halfway there. But as I walked toward the ball, angry, ball mark in hand and ready to mark what seemed to be a miserable effort, it started to get a second wind and pick up speed. "Dig, you dog," I said aloud as I watched my ball on its serpentine path across the green. "Hunt, puppy, hunt." Finally, the putt slid across the side of the cup, looking in as it did so. After winding its way around the cup, it settled at the bottom. I was more shocked then elated. I could stand on that green all day and not make a putt like that again. Was this really happening to me?

Then I started grinning. I just couldn't stop. I must have looked like the village idiot out there. Back-to-back birdies put me again to one over par.

At 363 yards, the 14th was a short par 4. I told myself not to fall asleep on this hole, because it would eat my shorts if I wasn't careful. It had water down the left side that eventually crossed in front of you farther down the fairway than I was willing to hit the ball. I laid up with my trusty 1 iron, leaving myself with 125 yards to the flag. Next, with a smooth 9 iron, I put it 12 feet from the cup. Then I put a good stroke on my putt, but lipped out. I made par easily. I was starting to have fun....not too much fun, mind you, but fun nonetheless.

The 15th hole could be a gimme par 5, if I could hit it far enough off the tee. I didn't even try, but as it happens, I hit one of my best drives of the day. I suppose that might tell you something about the importance of not trying too hard. Fifteen was a straightaway par 5, easily reached in 2 by the longer hitters. But there was a water hazard to contend with, running down the left side and then crossing in front of the green. A steep slope ahead the green and two cavernous bunkers made me think twice about hitting a long iron or fairway wood to the smallish green. I had about 200 yards to the green, and decided that if I was going to be back this year, I would be foolish to try for the green unless I absolutely had to. So I laid up with an 8 iron, then hit a sandwedge to the green. From 15 feet, I easily two-putted for my par. I had heard players say the 15 was a birdie hole, but breathing regularly for 15 minutes made the par worth it. Besides, I never thought par was a bad score anywhere on my scorecard.

The next hole was a long par 3, but I'm a good long iron player off the tee. I made a solid par, then was left with two holes to complete my round, both long and difficult par 4s. I got up and down from a bunker on 17, but missed a short putt for par on the last hole. I was glad it was over, though. And 74 was a very respectable score on that golf course. I was more than just a little proud of myself that day.

The next day, I would play Marborran, where scores averaged two shots lower than at Schofield Village. But even without taking into account the relative difficulty of each course, scorewise, I was on the bubble to make the top 64. I didn't want to think too much about it, but if I didn't let my imagination get the best of me at Marborran, I might have a chance.

t e n

As soon as I got off the course, I called Jane.

"Hi, honey, how are you feeling?"

"Fine, what did you shoot?" she said bluntly.

"What do you think I shot?"

"Oh, I'd say 74," she said. I could hear the smile in her voice.

I hated it when she did that. It especially pissed me off when she would say "81" and have hit it right on the head.

"How are you feeling?" I asked, changing the subject.

"Well, our first child might come any day now. But you shouldn't concern yourself about it, since you can't do anything about it anyway. Just play well, honey."

When I heard that, I was really peeved - but I wasn't sure why.

Was it because the fact that Jane was about to deliver gave me the perfect excuse to play poorly and miss the cut for match play? Was it selfish of me to be here, instead of at home with Jane? I started to wonder if it was myself I was peeved at.

Then I thought about why I was there in Ohio. The birth of my first child was certainly one of the most important events in my life, and I wanted very much to witness it. But wasn't it just as important to be able to tell my children, in 20 years, that their father had played in the U.S. Amateur?

After all, I wanted them to look up to me as a good example, as a role model. And I wanted them to pursue their dreams. They would say I had worked hard at my game, and gotten the job done. That I had made my dream reality. Wasn't this what was important in life?

I decided I couldn't allow contractions to sabotage my goals. It might sound awful, but Jane would have to live with that fact - and so would our children. I needed this chance to prove myself.

I stayed in my room all night, ordering dinner from room service. While watching a couple of movies, I stretched. I ate light and tried not to think of my next round at Marborran. After two good shots of scotch, I went to bed at 10 p.m. in preparation for my 10:15 a.m. tee time.

I awoke from the dead at 7 a.m., sharp. I know

that's what time it was because both the phone and my alarm clock started ringing at exactly that time. It was a slapstick comedy scenario: me, jumping out of bed and running to the phone - stubbing a toe in the process - to thank the wake-up recording I'd arranged the night before, then dashing back across the room - stubbing another toe in the process - to finally, fumblingly switch off the alarm clock.

Looking back on it, I realize my frenzied attempts to stop all that early-morning racket had a direct link to my relationship with my father. My father loved sleep, and whenever as a child I would wake him before he was ready, he'd get up and, half-drunk with sleep, one hand on his head and the other holding up his pajama bottoms, either give me a lickin' or at least scare the hell out of me.

Yawning myself awake, I prepared my drugs on the bathroom counter. First, I decided on two Bufferin to help loosen up my back, which was pretty stiff after a lot of golf and even more time on the range. Then I put an extra Bufferin in my pocket, just in case. Should I take my allergy pill today? I wondered next. I had taken one yesterday, but not the day before. I decided not to change my internal chemistry, and took the little white pill. How about the nose spray? I thought. I hated the nose spray. I always started sneezing and blowing my nose immediately after the nose spray. Today, I decided I would pass on the nose spray. But the eye-drops were a must. Always. Once in a while, my eyes would tear and itch, but mostly they were just dry. As a result, I relied on the eye-drops. I even kept extra drops in my golf bag; it's always good to refresh your eyes, especially during hay fever season - and for me, it was always hay fever season.

Next, I began stretching. I needed to stretch for at least 30 minutes. In turn, I tightened every muscle in my entire body - fists, butt, shoulders, every place I could focus on - taking a deep breath, holding it for 15 seconds or so, then letting go and relaxing, over and over again. Then I bent over at the waist, clasped my hands together behind my back. I raised my hands up, still clasped together, until my arms were perpendicular to the ground, stretching my back, shoulders, and arms. I tried to breathe evenly as I did these stretches, patience being a large part of the routine. I tried to go slowly, and give each yoga stretch I did equal dignity, as though it were the most important stretch of the day. But my mind was rather noisy that morning. I kept glancing at the clock, anxious to get out on the course. Finally, though, toward the end of my stretches, I began to feel relaxed.

My breakfast, mostly fruit, was light. I never eat during a round, and very little before it. Someone once told me that blood drains from your brain to digest the food in your stomach. For this round, I would need all the blood available swirling in my brain without wasting any in my stomach. I had never heard anyone complain about his stomach while playing bad golf, but I knew that I did stupid things all the time, so I didn't want to take any chance I would lose brain blood.

I drove very slowly to Marborran, arriving 59½ minutes before my tee time. Perfect! Warming up at the range, I hit most of the first 20 balls fat or thin. Eventually, though, it started to come around, and I was satisfied that I was properly warmed up.

The hum at Marborran was substantially lower than at Schofield the day before. There were no media towers or banners, for one thing. For another, the course was not roped off nearly as much. Spectators, the few who were there, seemed to know where to spectate from without upsetting anyone. This round would compose half the score one needed to qualify for match play, but it was obvious that Schofield would be remembered as the Amateur's venue.

I knew I would have to be careful on the so-called easier course, because any decent course can come up and bite you on the butt when you least expect it. The rough at Marborran was about the same as at Schofield, mostly playable with a mid to short iron for me, but at least at Marborran you had bail-out spots. Schofield had been considerably less forgiving, if not downright sadistic. You couldn't put all the blame on the course, however. One had to be a little masochistic to play it the way the USGA had set it up.

"Fairways, greens and two-putts, fairways, greens and two-putts," I chanted to myself on the way to the first tee. I didn't have to be low medalist. I just wanted to qualify for match play.

Finally, I heard my name called. I was more confident approaching the tee than I had been the day before. I had been more than slightly impressed by my play at Schofield. And today, at Marborran, my playing partners congratulated me on that round. Apparently, neither one of them had broken 75. For now, at least, I felt highly regarded.

I teed it high, hoping for a bunt shot anywhere in the first fairway. I just wanted to put it in play on this, my first hole. I timed my swing badly, and the ball started down the left side, off the neck of my driver, and sliced back to the right side of the fairway as I fell back.

My back swing had been tight and short, but there I was, in the fairway. Only 220 yards off the tee, but still, in the fairway.

For my next shot, I hit a 5 iron. Of course, the USGA expected everyone to hit a short iron to this green, and had placed the pin up in front, tucked in back of a bunker. I didn't care; I just wanted to hit the green - anywhere. I absolutely flushed my 5 iron. It must have carried 185 yards, almost 10 yards more than my usual 5 iron.

I was pumped. I had hit the fairway and the green on my first hole, but would have to contain myself for the 60-foot putt coming back. The putt broke generally from left to right, but speed would obviously be the crucial element. I hit it solidly on the intended line and momentarily daydreamed about it going in. A birdie on the first hole would be a great start! The ball slowed down as it approached the hole, and my heart nearly stopped as it caught the left corner. But instead of falling, it slung around the corner and stopped rolling 3 feet below the hole. Suddenly, I was thinking of what a bogey would do for me. At least the come-backer was uphill, slightly right to left. Not a hard putt, especially considering it was left over from a 60-footer. Not the tap-in I had imagined, but very makeable. I hit it firmly; the ball came off softly from the sweet spot on the putter face, and the stroke was as good as any I had ever made. No tension or grip grabbing, just

a moistness between my fingers. I looked up in time to see it hit the back of the cup, pop up and fall into the center of the hole. I wanted to stand there all day and feel the feeling I had watching it go in.

I drove the ball fairly well on the front nine at Marborran. I necked a few, but basically hit it straight - except for one shot that landed in the light rough. It wasn't U.S. Open rough, but it wasn't Rancho Park, either. I was still tight from nerves and couldn't seem to let it fly with reckless abandon. When those rare spans of time referred to as "the zone" were visited upon me, I would feel as if I was painting shots across the sky; my swing would feel as if I was dancing. "Oily" is a good word to describe how my joints would feel - none of the usual back pain would be present. I didn't feel any pain today, but I was really grinding. I even got a case of the 3-putts on 8 and 9, ending the front nine with a pair of bogeys.

The two boys playing with me were from Stanford and Wake Forest. The fellow from Wake Forest was struggling. I didn't keep his score, but he was at least 6 or 7 over par on the front nine. He was in pain, no doubt, and whatever he had, I didn't want to catch. I gave him a wide berth.

The young man from Stanford, also a senior, was cruising along pretty much the way I was, not picking up nor losing more than a shot or two to par. I felt safe making a little conversation with this kid without catching anything negative. He told me all about how his father had played on a Walker Cup team, made match play three out of four times at the Amateur, and also graduated Stanford. I could tell how proud he was of his father - yet, at the same time, his father's life seemed to weigh heavily on my young friend. It really made an impression on me. There I was, trying to make my unborn child proud of me - and this kid was trying to do the same thing for his father.

As the back nine started, I began calculating what my score could end up as, and what match I would play - before I had even qualified to play it. But knowing that thinking about what a score or outcome could be - or even worse, should be - was the kiss of death on the golf course during tournament play, I tried to change the mental radio station I was tuned to and put on something more reliable, like "fairways and greens." It was an old standard that helped me focus on "now." It worked fairly well - until the 16th hole.

I was 2 over for the day when I arrived at the 16th tee. The 16th hole was a cute, midsize par 3 over water. In the practice round, we had played the member's tee. I had hit an 8 iron to the back of the green. Now the tee was back 20 yards, and we were hitting to a pin in the center of the green. Smooth 6 iron, right? Sure, today we had a slight breeze in our face, but certainly no more than a firm 6 iron, right?

Well, I hit the 6 iron absolutely flush, right at the flag. "Eat it up!" someone in my threesome yelled. We watched the ball home in on the flag. It was going to be close! Back to one over again, I thought.....73, I imagined.

But then a deafening silence overcame the tee. I heard someone clear his throat on the 15th green. We all watched the ripples in the pond break up the reflection of the flag on the 16th green. I couldn't believe it. Was it possible that I had flushed a full 6 iron just 140 yards? It didn't make sense! Of course, it never makes sense when you think you're smart enough to know how and why golf shots work. The golf gods make sure you never fully understand this game. It's their game, and they're kind enough to allow you to play it - but only on their terms. And they have long memories. Even though I'd changed my mental radio station, I knew they had heard my blasphemous thoughts at the start of the back nine. Now they were

punishing me. My head got hot and cold at the same time as I started to perspire heavily. The ants were back, crawling around the top of my head again. My feet couldn't feel the ground, and all the sounds on the golf course at that moment sounded like the whir of a seashell you put to your ear when you want to hear the ocean.

I dropped a ball behind the water hazard and hit my 60-degree wedge. My heart was really pounding; I was certain you could see my chest pumping through my shirt if you looked closely enough. As you might have guessed, this shot also went into the pond.

At this point, complete dread filled my life. The ants made their steady way down my back and arms. My golfing life passed before my eyes. Still, there was nothing to do except hit a third ball. Changing clubs was unnecessary because when "they" were through with me "they" would let me know.

"Hit it close," Mikey said. "Don't give up." I resented hearing that from my squirt of a caddie. At her age, what could she know about failure?

I hit my 60-degree wedge again, and this time put it on the back of the green. No problem here, I thought sarcastically after walking to the green and standing over the putt. A downhill 30-footer that broke a kajillion ways, for triple bogey. So I just hit it, adopting an I-could-care-less attitude. After all, at this point it didn't seem to matter much, anyway. Without grinding at all, the ball wandered down the slope with perfect speed and casually dropped in the hole. My jaw dropped. Apparently, the golf gods had something in mind for me today, and I would have to play it out.

Feeling somewhat lightheaded after that triple bogey, I began to notice things I hadn't noticed before. For example, my caddy Mike seemed to come alive more than at any other time since I had hired her. At first, I had thought she was this cute kid from the neighborhood out to earn a few dollars. But slowly I was beginning to realize she was intensely interested in the outcome of the tournament, that she wanted very badly to be part of this week. She had admitted to an 11 handicap when I interviewed her initially, but she didn't try to compare her skills to anyone else's. She thought all the players here were special and that caddying for any one of them was an honor. And most important, she obviously wasn't about to let me feel sorry for myself.

I liked the way she just shook off the triple bogey on the next tee. No crybabies here, I thought, somewhat inspired. She just put the bag down and, holding onto the strap with her left hand, offered me a club with her right. "Play hard," she said with stern conviction. I knew she was right. I didn't resent the reminder.

It was easy to notice that my playing companions

were very quiet on the tee. Neither of them wanted anything I had to rub off on them. What could they say, anyhow? They saw my momentum as "down." Understanding this, I kept to myself.

I blocked my tee shot off the 17th tee. I was left with a severe sidehill lie that put my feet 2 feet below the ball, on a blind, 140-yard shot to the green. Choking down on a 7 iron, I swung away. I heard some excitement at the green from the small gallery (my playing partners' two sets of parents), and figured it was probably on. When I approached the green, I heard a couple "nice shots" from the players. The ball was 10 feet from the hole.

"I could make this putt," I said to no one in particular. I winked at Mikey. She ignored the wink, her expression telling me to get down to business.

My putt was off the heel, but kept the line. Would it be enough? Moving at cup speed, the ball just barely dropped in. My heart nearly stopped as I watched it; I was beginning to think I was a little too old for this sort of thing. Only force of habit made me walk to the next tee. One thing was certain, I wasn't adding my score in my head. I had already learned that lesson for the millionth time. But still I knew I needed to make birdie on this last hole.

I had honors, but was tempted to give them up to slow my heartbeat down a little. It was racing. But I hit away, sending a good drive to the heart of the fairway. I really beat on it! Up on the green, the pin was tucked in the back left corner. Perfect! I could hit a draw, my natural shot with a 7 iron: 157 yards. I could swing away. I was pumped! I struck the ball well, and it started to draw from the center of the green towards the flag. "Get down!" I yelled. The ball one-hopped on the green, landing in the green-side back bunker. Making things worse, I saw when

I got up to the bunker, the ball was buried on a severe slope, with no real play to the hole.

Oh well, I thought, there's no reason to be mad at "myself." It was "them." It was always "them." I put a good swing on it and got a bad break. "Play it out and don't take worse than bogey," I muttered. That's great! I thought. Now I'm talking to myself! I got into the bunker with a sense of resignation, and with my stance considerably above the ball, aiming 10 to 15 feet right of the flag, I started the club back. With a half-swinging, half-jerking motion, I excavated the ball from its sandy dungeon. The ball yanked left, hot out of the bunker, and hit the top of the flag dead center. And then, amazingly, it dropped right into the hole.

My whole body was shaking. The senior from Wake Forest, silent most of the day, said, "Good comeback, 75?" a bit disoriented, I nodded. When my feet finally felt like they were back on the ground, I signed my card (after checking it about 20 times) and handed it in. After I did, surprisingly, Mikey, on her tippy toes, gave me a hug and a peck on the cheek.

"Good job," she said.

Now I would have to wait to see whether I would make match play tomorrow, or fly home tonight, on what promised to be the loneliest flight of my life. Over at Command Central at Schofield, Mikey and I waited out the results. We sat under a tree about 40 feet from the scoreboard and watched them post two-day scores from both courses. An arrow pointed to the projected cut. It was at 152 now, but I knew it would come down. I was safe at 149 for the moment, but many scores had not yet been posted.

When the arrow was moved to 151, I could hear a bunch of players audibly groan - the sound of dreams breaking.

Then the arrow was moved again, to 150. I was getting sick. I couldn't catch my breath. There were seven of us at 149.

Finally, with a couple groups still out on the course, it became mathematically clear there would be a play-off between the seven players at 149. Now the question was, how many spots?

Once the last group tallied their scores, there were ten players at 149, for nine spots. All I could think about was the poor soul who would not get one of the nine spots. Some golfers might never recover from that kind of disappointment. Myself included? I didn't want to find out.

I figured par on the first playoff hole would be a good score. I'll never forget what it was like as all ten of us teed off the first hole at Schofield Village. It didn't seem fair to those of us who had played Marborran that day to have our playoff at Schofield, but it wasn't as if we hadn't seen the course before. I quickly put that thought out of my mind; it was one of those things that could be used as an excuse, if you needed one to fail.

I hit a solid drive, then a 6 iron to the first green, about 35 feet away. All I had to do was 2-putt and go back to my hotel to prepare for tomorrow's match. Several other players were in trouble and would probably make bogie or worse.

As we approached the green, a heavy-set fellow with dark hair walking in the fairway next to me caught my attention. He was about my age, maybe a bit older. His large, fleshy hands held a wedge, and he was wearing last year's U.S. Amateur logo on his shirt. Was he really who I thought he was? Was that Jay Meyer, the two-time former U.S. Amateur Champion? He had won the U.S. Mid Amateur three times, as well, and numerous other prestigious amateur invitationals around the country. In the minds of many, he was unquestionably one of the game's best amateurs.

"Nice shot," he said, without looking at me. I was flattered that he had noticed me. "Two putts and you're in - good luck." He softly patted me on the shoulder and headed for the edge of the fairway.

Jeez, I can't tell you how great his presence felt! It made me feel like I was in the club.

I lined up my putt carefully, in the hope of giving myself a tap-in par. I didn't feel a lot of pressure, but still the putt was difficult enough. My heart was working double time today. My chest actually throbbed. I put a good stroke on it and rolled the ball about 2 feet by the hole. Certainly no tap-in, but still pretty manageable. I had to wait interminably to putt out. During the wait, I tried to line up the putt several times, but each time other players got in my way. I got reads off of several putts that led me to believe my own putt was fairly straight. By the time it was my turn, no one had made double bogey. I had to make it or go to the next hole with the bogeymen. I decided to hit it straight, firm. I looked down at the ball and noticed I was holding my breath. Should I hold my breath? I had never given it much thought, but suddenly had to decide what to do about it before making my stroke. Then, magically, my mind seemed to quiet down, and I forgot all about my breath. I witnessed the stroke. Moments later, I realized I had made it. And when I turned to Mikey, she had what might be called a wry smile on her face.

Jay Meyer was the first person to congratulate me.

eleven

After the playoff, I was on a natural high. I thought about the sheer numbers associated with the U.S. Amateur Championship. Approximately 5,000 entries had been sent to the USGA for this tournament. Of that number, only 312 players had qualified at local sites around the country. Qualifying for match play had whittled the number down to 64 contestants. In a few days, we would have our champi-on. But for now, I was happy to be one of the 64 best amateur golfers in America.

I wanted to be alone tonight. I also wanted to share this moment with Jane, because she loved me and deserved whatever pleasure she might derive from my success. But secretly, I really wanted to be alone. It had to do with the way I had been brought up - lonely, or at least alone.

I wanted to feel connected to Jane, and certainly to my baby; but for the most part, any connection I would feel tonight would be contrived. Tonight I just wanted to love myself. To cherish each memory from the past two days on the golf course. The bright yellow ropes restraining the crowds; the TV towers covered with banners. All the shots I had made when I really needed them. This was what golf was all about. No matter who's rooting for you, in the end, it's a solitary game.

Just prior to taking the Bar, I promised myself that if I passed I would always consider myself a success, no matter what. Boy, it sure is easy to forget the promises you make to yourself! I didn't consider myself a failure by any means, but being a lawyer wasn't what I'd had in mind when it was a dream of mine. I had thought it would mean more,

for longer than it did. I had been naive enough to think that any feelings of worth that came from passing the Bar might last a lifetime. I was surely wrong about that. After my round at Marborran, however, I was confident that the feeling I had from making match play might very well last to the end of my life. Someone once told me that you can never own the game, you can just borrow it from time to time. You can never tell if you'll hit another high, soft-cutting 3 iron to a front right pin again. It's that kind of game. It's more or less like life in that respect.

Back in my room, I spoke to Jane. She was so excited, she wanted to get off the phone and start calling her family and friends. This is the way people who love act, I thought to myself. You would have thought she had made match play, the way she carried on. This is the way normal people who love you act. I could learn from this, I thought to myself. I could really learn from this.

Later, Jane called back to tell me what everyone she'd talked to had said. I listened patiently as she went down the list of everyone who wanted her to congratulate me, to tell me they loved me. Why did they tell me they loved me now? How did they feel about me before? But it all seemed perfectly natural to Jane, so I took her lead and pretended to accept all the love and affection being hurled my way. She was so excited, I was afraid she might drop the puppy at any moment. I told her to calm down and wait for me before having any puppies. She promised me she would.

As we spoke, I found myself missing her intensely. We spoke about love, life and living, for more than an hour. I guess I really didn't want to be alone, after all.

Jane talked on and on about how proud of me she was, and I could see her face in my mind. Then, when it was my turn to speak, I tried to explain all that I had seen or experienced. About the boy from Stanford whose father had played in all those Amateurs, and the Walker Cup besides. Would our son or daughter feel the pressure this boy had felt out there today? I tried to express those thoughts and emotions, but was unsure I was making myself clear - or even what it was I really wanted to say. At the end of the conversation, I knew just one thing for sure: I didn't want to be alone at all. What I would have given to have Jane hug me just then.

twelve

The next day at Schofield, there was a ceremonial send-off at the first tee. All I could think about was not bogeying the first hole of my first match. My opponent should have to birdie to beat me on the first hole, I thought.

A junior at Arizona State, my opponent had qualified six shots from the medalist. The good news about qualifying for match play and progressing to quarterfinals was that you could come back the following year as exempt. The bad news about just making the cut was that you ended up with a top seed as your first match. Physically, my opponent was only a bit larger than I was, but he had the appearance of tremendous strength. He obviously trained with weights. I noticed his hands and arms, in particular; one could not acquire such hands and arms without working with weights. He had shot 68 on his second day, at Marborran, a great comeback after shooting 75 at Schofield Village. I was impressed. Many other players with as much talent but less grit might have given up and simply gone through the motions in the second round.

I hit a good drive off the first tee, leaving myself 176 yards to a big green. Quite a good shot, considering I was looking at a par 4 446-yard monster. A smooth 6 iron to the center, and two putts later I had set up my round. I was going to be tough!

And I was going to have to be. My opponent had hit it 40 yards past me off the first tee. After that, I promised myself I would not watch him swing or follow his ball. Oh, I would help him look for an errant shot, if need be, but I did not want to get into a homerun contest with this brute. Besides, a few friends of his were in the gallery; they could find his ball no matter how deep in the woods he would hit it.

I decided to speak only when spoken to. This fellow was a serious contender; he had more than a few followers, and I didn't want to seem like I was in awe of him. I wanted my sticks to do all my talking. I wanted to appear confident and busy at work. I didn't want him to see me shake or notice the fear in my eyes, if it was at all noticeable. I don't know if I ended up coming off that way, but it's the way I decided to proceed in the match.

I didn't give much away during this round. My putting was solid, but I didn't make anything beyond 12 feet or so, and only a couple of those. I hit it within 20 to 30 feet of the flag most of the day, tapping in short second putts. Those greens I did miss, I didn't miss by much, and I chipped close enough to get up and down. My opponent and I were never more than one hole up or down to each other - until the 17th. I had made mostly all pars, and he had made mostly birdies and bogeys. He was one down.

As we approached the 17th tee, I happened to notice he wasn't in the socializing mood anymore. The 17th hole was 430 yards, with a long bunker bordering the left side of the fairway. If you hit it too far to the right off the tee, you would be blocked out by trees on the right side of the fairway, 50 yards short of the green. I tried to hit it down the middle (don't we all!) but hooked it into the left fairway bunker, 205 yards from the center of the green. Then I made my first mistake: noticing where my opponent hit his drive - 140 yards from the green. And my second mistake was failing to remember how I had gotten this far. I was absolutely convinced he would make 4 or better. Suddenly, I was afraid of going into 18 even up.

I didn't think I could hit a long iron to the green from where I was in the bunker; that's something they only do on TV. I should have tried, however, to advance the ball to within 40 yards of the green, to possibly get it to the front bib or extended collar for a fairly straightforward pitch, which would have given me a chance to putt for par. This could have been done with a 5 iron. It would have been smart and doable.

Instead, I took out my 5 wood. And, of course, I hit it in the deep right greenside bunker. I was only 30 feet away from the flag, but that bunker was really deep. My opponent hit it about 25 feet away, but above the hole. As I approached the green, my face was tingling, and I realized that I was grinding my teeth. I thought of all the great bunker shots I had made before, and told myself I needed one more here. I stepped into the bunker and set my feet. I actually had a good lie. But then I watched the club go back a few inches, and it really threw me off. Not exactly your basic sandtrap fundamental. And, of course, the ball hit the bank in front of me, then rolled back down into my footprint

"Thank God for match play!" I said to myself. It was only one hole; I might lose my advantage, but I wouldn't lose the match - at least not here. With a big, chopping action, I got out of the trap, just on the fringe of the green. I was all but conceding the hole to my opponent, but still had to go through the motions. My mind was already on the 18th tee.

I could see it on his face, in his eyes. I can't describe exactly what it was, except to say it was something that's a little different, and I definitely knew it was there. My opponent was anticipating my collapse, and he couldn't hide it. He shouldn't do that, at least not yet, I thought. I've been offered up as an example by the golf gods before, for much lesser offenses.

Mikey stood motionless across the green. She did not move to hand me my putter or pull the flag. She wasn't my caddie anymore, she had become a spectator. For the first time that day she was enthralled by the goings-on.

I lie 4, he lies 2, and now he's away. I was sure he thought he was going to make that first putt. He must have thought that because he knocked it 4 feet past the hole. Suddenly, his demeanor changed; he was upset. And rightly so. He should have lagged that putt and played for a tap-in two-putt. No easy feat to two-putt for all the marbles from 25 feet, but it was certainly time to be on the cautious side. Of course, I did lie 4, but I was only 16, maybe 17 feet away. I told Mike to take the pin out. When she did not respond from her daze, I walked over to the flag and gently removed it myself. She still did not react.

I had a good lie and put the sand wedge up on its toe, back in my stance. I picked out a spot on the green to land the ball. I played this shot to check slightly and roll the rest of the way to the hole. Gripping the club with my usual putting grip, I took the club back. I made an efficient stroke that landed the ball right on the spot I had picked out. It checked once and rolled nicely...right into the hole.

The golf gods, I knew, were using me as an instrument to blunt my opponent's arrogance. They might not have appreciated my stubbornness, but they for damn sure didn't like arrogance. Even now, I can't figure what happened next: My opponent missed the hole with his putt coming back.

Going to 18, I was still one up. The match wasn't over yet, but I had showed a few people my mettle.

On the 18th hole, my opponent's first tee shot very nearly made it into orbit. He put some major red ass on it. We would never find it, it was so far out of bounds. And then, he hooked his second ball into the water hazard on the left side of the fairway.

Meanwhile, I hit it very weakly in the fairway. Then I helped him look for his ball. When we found it in the hazard and saw it could not be played, he turned to me and shook my hand. He couldn't look me in the face, but I knew it wasn't arrogance or bad sportsmanship this time. I think he was teary-eyed. His dream, after all, was over.

I know I was teary-eyed. My dream was a work in progress.

thirteen

My fourth round in the Amateur, and I was still pretty nervous while waiting to approach the first tee. It was amazing, my capacity for experiencing anxiety. The night before, I had once again talked to Jane, pouring out my fears; my back might seize up before a big shot; I might forget how to get to the golf course in the morning; I would win the match in just 10 holes, only to be disqualified for filling out my card incorrectly. I was so nervous, I had taken my clubs with me back to the hotel room, fearful they might be stolen at Schofield Village.

Once again, Jane had let me vent, then reminded me to remember the skill and determination that had gotten me here. God, I wished she were here with me. Today was going to be grueling. Today, I was playing another PGA Tour-bound kid. But today, if I could get through this match, I would have another match in the afternoon. No, you couldn't take a cart, and there would be no time to nap between matches. I liked to walk, but 36 holes in one day would be a lot for this buggy on these wheels.

My opponent was one of the favorites in this year's event. Here I was playing another school kid, and for the second time, I had heard of him from the box scores in *Golf World* Magazine. But then again, I chuckled to myself, I doubt he has ever heard of a Chapter 11 "Cram down" or "Relief from the Automatic Stay." In fact, if he can't beat me, he better start learning some of that crap. He would need it when he finished school.

Despite a minor slump that had received a lot of publicity, he had managed to qualify most respectfully at 143, one under par. The media and his school coach were "hopeful." Although he was one of the top seeds in the medal qualifying, his first match had been a squeaker. So was he out of his highly publicized "slump" yet? There were telltale signs, apparently, that his winning form had not yet returned. In his first match, he had played an "unknown" who took him to the 21st hole before succumbing. And now here I was (another unknown) standing on the first tee with him - potentially the next U.S. Amateur Champion. I felt like chopped liver standing there, listening to ESPN interview him about his plans after the Amateur. Would he go pro? Et cetera.

If I lost, I decided, I wanted him to win the tournament. That way, I could tell my son or daughter that I had lost to the champion. If he went on to become a famous pro, maybe I could take my kid(s) to see him at our local golf extravaganza, the Los Angeles Open. Maybe each year, he would let us inside the ropes, where he and I could reminisce.

Each year, I would make him laugh by making a mock demand for a rematch. He would tell me how much Patrick/Patty had grown.

I felt like an idiot after this daydream was over. I should have been daydreaming about my golf game, about great shots I could hit, instead of a bunch of mental trash.

Already, at 7:30 a.m., play was backed up. I could never understand how some of the best players could play so slowly, especially in a format in which they didn't always putt out. While we waited to be called to tee off, I studied my opponent. He was my size. Size was the first thing you noticed if you were 5'9" and never felt you hit it long enough (I know about driving for show and putting for dough, but these days the guys who putt for all the dough also hit it 280 yards on a string). He - his name was Billy - just didn't look special to me.

And that didn't change when we got out on the course. I was three over par after five holes, yet only one down. He wasn't exactly running me over, although he had many opportunities. I thought maybe he was saving it for when he needed it; and the way I was hitting it, he wouldn't need it anytime soon.

Still, there was something quality about him. Confidence. You could see it on his face. He was patient with his mistakes. He was biding his time, waiting to play his next match. This match with the geezer would be over soon enough; after it, he could go to the range and straighten out whatever problem he was having that day. Meanwhile, he would take care of the matter at hand with what he had brought to the first tee, and saving the rest for when he needed it....for the real test to come.

Noticing this, I didn't get angry or depressed. I

didn't get all fired up, either; it didn't piss me off one bit. I just kept grinding, trying to make the best showing I could. Then came the 12th hole. At that point, I was five over, two down to Billy the Kid. The 12th hole, you might recall, was a replica of the 12th hole at the Masters. Water in front and to the right of the green, a bunker in front and a bunker back left. Miss the shot, and you could find the drink or the sand.

Blocking his first shot, my opponent found the water. Then he skulled the next one over the green, into the back bunker. I was looking like bogey when Billy attempted his shot out of the back bunker. He skulled it again, but this time into the water. And not only had he lost the hole, he had lost his sense of confidence. That look in his eye? Suddenly, it was gone, replaced by a look of fear. Apparently, he had yet to learn that winning ugly still counts. I, on the other hand, was not embarrassed to stink up the place with frayed nerves and shoddy technique. I relished the moment, because I was not supposed to win; I just wanted to hang around as long as I could.

The next hole was a long dogleg left, par 4. You started with a drive through a wooded chute to a narrow fairway. I healed my drive, skenking it out there about 240 yards (it was slightly downhill) but in the fairway. My opponent, meanwhile, couldn't even make it through the wooded chute. His ball, in fact, ended up lost for good. After this hole, I realized that he was already in the proverbial clubhouse. He was burning with shame. Meanwhile, I was trying very hard to rededicate myself to those basic strategies that had served me well before. I tried to withdraw into myself, to be totally absorbed by what I was doing. We were now even going into 14; anything could happen.

Fourteen was a cute little par 4, that required a

lay-up off the tee, due to a creek on the left that eventually crossed the fairway. I hit a 2 iron off the tee, thin and off the heel: my basic skenk shot down the middle of the fairway, about 220 yards out (yes, it was firm, downhill). My young friend, unfortunately for him, sent his shot out to the right, followed by your basic, sniping hook. In the creek. Even though I made bogey, he made a dreaded "other," and I was finally one up on the match, going into 15.

I had not formulated my victory speech (even an old fool like me knows better than that). From my viewpoint, there was still a lot of life left in this match. The "Mo," however, was definitely with me. I could see my opponent literally talking to himself.

fourteen

The next hole was a shortish par 5 at 490 yards. I saw no reason to try and hit the green in two and potentially make 7. There was trouble everywhere. So I hit a 2 iron off the tee and a 5 iron to about 75 yards from the flag. Billy did much the same thing, laying back to about 100 yards. We both got it on, but I was out at 20 feet, while he was 10 feet from the hole.

By this point, I was shaking. My sand wedge swing had been extremely stiff; I actually found the green with an unintended cut shot. By contrast, Billy's swing on the approach had looked fluid and crisp. I wondered if he could smell my fear. Was he paying any attention to me at all? I wished I could hide in a corner of his mind and listen, if for only a minute or two.

I was the first to putt. It was pretty straight, but I couldn't tell if it was uphill or downhill. I had absolutely no idea about the speed of this putt. A great situation, given that this could be the putt of the match.

The putter went off in my hands. I knew I had killed it. As soon as I hit it, I dropped to my knees and yelled, "Hit the hole!" If it didn't hit the hole, I knew, I'd be 10 or 15 feet past it. But it did hit the hole, hard, bouncing off the back lip, straight up, then straight down. The ball disappeared into the hole, and I heard Billy exhale as though he had been punched in the stomach. He slouched over, leaning on his putter. I didn't say a word. Unbelievable, I thought, feeling my body vibrate with the surge of adrenaline. I held up my right hand in front of me, watching it tremble.

Billy stalked his putt as though it might be his last. And rightly so; if he missed it, I would be two up with three holes to play. Were the golf gods on my side today? Had they chosen me over the potential superstar? I tried to banish such thoughts from my mind. I didn't want to provoke them.

Seconds later, Billy's ball slid by the hole looking in. Clearly a better effort, with clearly inferior results.

We both parred the next long par 3 hole, and now I had Billy "dormied" or two down with two to go. Suddenly, the press was with us, because of the upset possibilities. I hoped some of it would get airtime, so Jane and my family could remember how good I once was. Then I thought about our VCR, and how often Jane screwed up recording programs. Maybe it would be better that way, I thought - especially if I botched this next hole. But that was not to be. Instead, Billy and I both bogeyed the hole in undramatic fashion. I won, two up with one to go. The dream continued.

fifteen

I tried to call Jane before my next match. I wanted to hear her voice, her excitement. I needed her encouragement, since I was more wracked by anxiety then I'd ever been because of golf. I had just defeated one of the tournament favorites! But I didn't know what it was I was feeling, joy or fear or... I didn't know. All I knew was that the cream was rising to the top, and I was rising with it while trying not to drown or choke.

I finally reached Jane at her mother's house. She wanted to come to Ohio, but we both knew she couldn't. I needed her more than ever, but the health of the baby had to come first and chancing delivery on the plane was ridiculous. (I did think about it, though. Maybe even hinted a little. In my heart of hearts, I figured I would be home soon enough, anyway.) It was great just to talk to her. Once again, talking to her calmed my excitement and dread.

After a very light lunch, I went back out to the course. I would be playing last year's NCAA Champion. Now was the time to start trying to believe my own stuff. I had to, because I was really scared of humiliating myself. Why was I so scared? Golf is a game, for Christ's sake! It's supposed to be fun! Am I having fun? Clearly, I was not having fun. I made a promise to myself that I wouldn't compete outside of my Sunday foursome if I could just get through this gracefully.

But then I thought, who am I kidding? If I couldn't compete, I wouldn't even bother to play. I didn't believe for a moment that I could be casual about my game....or anything, for that matter. But then, what would happen when my newborn arrived? When I was suddenly faced with a whole new heap of responsibilities - things like changing diapers? How would I ever manage to compete then? I took a deep breath, realizing suddenly that my mind was on the verge of spinning out of control. Right now, I needed calm, relaxation. So I decided to hit the range.

I was swinging like an automaton at the range. I had to slow down, all the way down. I was really hyper; my tempo was fast and my grip tight, so I stopped hitting balls and tried some yoga breathing exercises to help calm myself down. It sort of worked. After stretching awhile, I went over to the putting green. There, a Blue Coat summoned me to the USGA tent.

"Uh-oh," I thought.

A Blue Coat is one of those guys who volunteers

to marshal or give rulings at a tournament, otherwise known as a USGA committee member. By definition, Blue Coats are crusty old WASPs with substantial leisure time to commit to USGA events. These guys wield a great deal of power when rendering decisions and rulings. Even if one made a bad call, once he said you were gone, you were gone. So, of course, I got paranoid. This older gentlemen in the blue coat, white shirt and blue-and-red striped tie could not be good news, and he wanted me to come with him.

When I arrived at the tent, everyone looked grim. My heart was in my throat. What had I done wrong? I thought, my face burning. "We've got a problem," the old man told me. Oh, hell, I thought. I figured there was a technical difficulty with my scorecard. In any case, I was certain I was in deep "mobo," if they wanted me at this proceeding. On the other hand, this could be just the excuse I was looking for.

"I was going to win the Amateur back in "91," when the Blue Coats disqualified me."

But my fears were ill-founded. My next opponent had already attested his scorecard, and they wanted me to sign it as scorer. Apparently, my match was over before it even began. It seemed the former NCAA Champion had hurt his wrist on a tree root late in his morning round and simply couldn't hold a club anymore. The Blue Coat reached for my hand to congratulate me, and I immediately thought, "Do you get to go to the Masters as a quarterfinalist?"

s i x t e e n

A few years earlier, quarterfinalists had gone to the Masters, that special tournament known even to those usually unfamiliar with golf. Amen Corner, Magnolia Lane, the beautiful dogwoods and azaleas. Most folks have seen these sights and know something of the rich history of the Masters. But by the time I made the U.S. Amateur, only finalists were granted an invitation to that most celebrated of all golf tournaments - a fact I bemoaned for a good part of my Thursday evening. I tried to take solace that nowadays, quarterfinalists did have their matches televised on cable, but somehow, exposure on cable TV did not measure up to an invitation to the Masters. I couldn't help but feel a little cheated. Of course, prior to this evening, I would have welcomed the idea of feeling cheated out of a Masters invitation because I had made the quarterfinals of the U.S. Amateur.

Despite the stiff drink I had before bed, I could not fall asleep. My head was really buzzing! The drinks must have been stiffer in Bobby Jones' day. Finally, I nodded off for a couple of hours. But then I awoke again in the middle of the night, my mouth filled with the crappy aftertaste of liquor and my head filled with golfmares. I thought about another drink, but I was afraid of waking up with a hangover, if indeed I even got back to sleep at all. I hated staying up all night. The next day's match would be tough enough with a good night's sleep, but next to impossible if I was only half awake and slightly spaced out. Getting back into bed, I put the pillow between my arms and crumpled it up the way I liked it. If I couldn't sleep, I would at least try to rest.

When wake-up time came, I ached like hell. I had played a lot more golf then I had imagined I would. In fact, I had thought I would be home by now, helping Jane with breathing exercises or some Eastern massage technique she had been pestering me about.

After a light breakfast and my usual drug routine, I drank a mixture of regular and decaffeinated coffee to help me get loose. Then I stretched, and stretched, and stretched. Then, fully clothed, I went down to the sauna and stretched again. After working up a mild sweat, I finally started to loosen up. Even though it was a cool summer morning, I was sweating like a pig as I walked through the hotel lobby on my way to the golf course.

Finally, after hitting balls and putting for an hour, I started to come alive. It was like walking a tightrope that morning: I was trying to wake myself up enough to be fully alert, but at the same time I was trying to calm myself so I wouldn't get over-nervous at the first tee. After that, it would all be automatic pilot. Or so I hoped.

Before my quarterfinal match, I was interviewed by magazine reporters and filmed by camera crews. The hardest part about it all was answering questions about my family. Should I tell the media about the fact that I had a newborn on the way? I wasn't sure - and, at that point, I knew I was feeling at least some shame over leaving Jane when my child was about to be born. I thought about pro golfers I'd heard of who had skipped the Masters, PGA, British Open or U.S. Open to witness the birth of their children. I told myself that their situation was quite different from mine. After all, they would play these tournaments again in their careers. I, on the other hand, couldn't be certain I would ever qualify for, much less get to, the quarterfinals of the U.S. Amateur again. As far as I was concerned, it was a one in 5000 shot.

I won't drone on with too many details of how it in went on the course that day. I only want to say it was rhythm, timing, poetry and art. I was on. If feeling great over the ball on every swing is being in "the zone," I was there. Nothing hurt. No weird bounces, and a few friendly ones, came my way. The ball seemed to roll close after even the most awkward of shots. Sounds easy, doesn't it? It was. The ball just rolled close. No 4-foot comebackers or lipouts from 2 feet. I didn't make any cross-country putts, but managed a few 15-footers. In essence, I played some of the best golf of my life. I was neat and tidy around the greens, and very relaxed off the tee. I drove the ball superbly and with plenty of distance. I was in complete control of my ball. I worked it left or right as needed.

Strangely, I felt utterly alone on the course as I played. It was funny; all my life, I'd dreaded loneliness, yet there I was on the golf course, enjoying feeling more alone than ever. I didn't notice anyone around me until the 16th hole of the quarterfinal match. At that point, I realized that a crowd had gathered around me, and that everyone wanted to shake my hand. Quickly, I figured out what had happened: I had won my match.

In my semifinal match, it was more of the same. It was great not to have to putt out all the time.

I think my opponents played well, but I really wasn't paying much attention. Why? I had a "no consequences" attitude. Whatever I did or didn't do had no consequences to me. Wherever the ball would go or did not go, I didn't attach a positive or negative consequence to it. I had virtually no expectations; or if I did, I kept them extremely well hidden from myself. I just golfed my ball, trying to enjoy each shot for what it had to offer. I felt so clean, so pure. I'm sure the USGA wanted to drug test me after those two matches. I didn't have to make excuses for my opponents; I just flat-out beat them. They just didn't play as well as I did.

Jay Meyer had been beaten in the round of 16 and was now following my semi-final match. He kept telling me I was on a roll. His presence was very reassuring and encouraging. I told myself it was as though he could tell who the next champion was going to be, because he had been there twice, and he had learned to be a witness of the events unfolding. His spirits didn't seem down, even though he would not witness himself winning this year. He could accept the decision of the golf gods as easily as he accepted their largesse in years past.

At the end of that second round, I felt like I was able to see and feel things about myself I had never known before. For example, I realized that, since my life had been in chaos for as long as I could remember, chaos management was a skill I had developed - and learned to use on the golf course. So I was able to take advantage of seemingly out-of-control situations on the course, where other supposedly stronger players would just fall apart.

I also realized that, on the whole, I had a good relationship with fear. Fear motivated me. The fear of being exposed as a fraud on the golf course, for instance, had pushed me forward, motivated me to continue playing - to prove to the world I was not a fraud.

And then, there was the issue of my mortality. The kids I was playing with still didn't realize that they would die some day. At 21 or 22. mortality simply isn't an issue. At my age, mortality comes into focus sharply. I had very few years left to perform on this level. It had taken me more than 40 years to get here - I wasn't about to just give all that away, without seeing exactly what I could accomplish.

Back at the hotel, I learned that the following day would not only be the final of the U.S. Amateur - it might also mark my debut as a father. I talked to Jane, and her contractions had begun. I felt such a fool bothering her about some silly golf match when our baby was about to be born. But, somehow, I believed there was a connection between the two events.

I told Jane I might be able to make it home in time if I came straight after this last match, and she promised she would do her best to hang on until I arrived.

s e v e n t e e n

The next morning, I was wracked by doubt about whether I should play. How could I, with my beloved wife about to give birth? I could've called the USGA and told them I was going home. The vice president of United States probably would have given me a medal for family values. But then, I thought about the repercussions of pulling out of the tournament. Did I want to be one of those guys who were famous for what they didn't do? The USGA and cable TV would be steamed. The other semifinalist would make history as the victor, but with a compromising footnote. He would also have a right to be steamed. It's possible I would be banned from competition. And for what? Jane would probably have had the baby before I even got home.

Finally, I settled down. The day was ethereal. Perfect golf weather, overcast but not cold, about 75 degrees, with a bit of humidity to oil my joints. In California, we call it earthquake weather. Everything seemed so still, so quiet. I felt great; nothing hurt.

As the round started, I noticed Mikey. She was doing a great job. For the first time, this dear child was grinning from ear to ear. She had made it to the final match; she had reached her goal.

Studying Mikey more closely I could see she was someone's baby. I could see that more clearly than ever. I tried not to stare at her too much, but I couldn't help but notice how young her hands were as she dried my clubs. Her skin seemed so perfect, with a cute little blond fuzz visible here and there. Maybe these were the beginning of paternal feelings that would grow within me as my baby grew.

Mikey had been a beautiful baby; someone's beautiful baby.

I wondered what feelings my father had when he looked at his son, his successful, big deal lawyer, son. Blocking out the memory of my father lying in that hospital room with tubes and wires coming out of him, I tried to imagine him as a proud father in the gallery, quietly yet confidently supporting the efforts of his son, agonizing over every shot that didn't come off as planned, intending to be there for me in the end, regardless of the day's outcome. That's the kind of father I wanted to be, the kind of father I had always wanted for myself.

I played conservatively and was solid over the ball all morning, carding a 2-under 70 round. At the turn, I was two up on the match.

I was three up on the match until the 16th hole

of the afternoon round (my 34th hole), where I lost the hole to birdie. You couldn't really say I was choking just by losing a hole, but it felt like the clubhouse was a million miles away, and thoughts of choking were certainly creeping into the back of my mind. I kept hearing the TV announcer in my head, saying that this tournament was mine to win or lose. But I put these thoughts and others of equally no significance out of my mind and kept playing Old Man Par. I would just play the golf course and try not to beat myself.

After 16, the sky started to darken as thick clouds completely obscured the sun. Oh, no, I thought. The last thing I wanted was a postponement. I wanted to finish today no matter what. I wanted to be with Jane. I wanted to go home and be a father.

At 17, I was still two shots up. But I had just lost to a birdie, and lost my honors. Had I lost my momentum, as well? I tried not to think about it.

Seventeen was one of the toughest par 4s on the course. I knew that par would be a good score. The hole was 430 yards long, with a bunker down the entire left side landing area. Hitting it right would mean at least a bogey, since the rough was heavy and trees blocked any approach to the elevated green. It was a force carry shot that only the guy who designed the course could hit from the rough. Deep rough and a grass bunker precluded a simple pitch from just in front of the green. Danger to the left; danger to the right. This was a critical tee shot for me.

My opponent teed off first. He hit a 1 iron absolutely perfectly, about 250 yards or so down the center of the fairway. Obviously, he wasn't about to let me have a tie with a bogey. At the same time, he was giving himself a chance at birdie. After all, he was two down with two to play. He also knew that par would be a good score here, and that I wasn't long enough to hit an iron off the tee. He was doing a good job of keeping the pressure on me.

The 3 wood would not have been a good play for me. My 3 wood was really a 4 wood that the manufacturer called a 3 wood, so guys like me could say we hit a high 3 wood. I actually hit my 1 iron farther, with the roll factored in - especially here where the ground was hard and the grass short (in the fairway). But I had a lot of confidence in my driver. Even when I skenked it, I skenked it straight. I wanted to hit my tee shot past my opponent, since the pressure would (in my mind) shift to him if I did - but I would have to be in the fairway. I wanted to force him to try and hit it close to the flag, which was located back left on the green, six steps from the end of the

world. So the driver it was.

I took some extra time with this shot, trying to let every twitch in my body resolve itself before taking the club back. I stepped away, then started again. Once again, perspiration started pouring down my nose. Stepping away again, I wiped my face with my shirtsleeve. Not great TV, but it would have to do. Setting up again, I tried to relax every muscle in my arms and hands - especially my hands. I watched the club go back, but somehow never took my eye off the ball. The club head ripped through the ball, its momentum literally making me reflex back, a la Arnie. My knees buckled as the ball flew right, then began gently to draw back left. It had felt as good as it looked. This astronaut was in control of his missile.

Walking off the tee, I started to think of Jane, so I tried to not think of Jane. I needed the next 15 minutes or so just for me. I would sort out these feelings about me, Jane and the baby later. I wanted to win for my baby. I wanted to tell my baby that was what I was trying to do - win it for him, or her. As soon as that thought entered my mind, though, I knew I was lying. I wanted to win for me.

I had outdriven my opponent by 20 yards and was in the left center of the fairway. I could not have placed it better. It looked like a smooth 6 iron to the left center of the green and then two easy putts.

As my opponent addressed his ball, I watched without really watching. I wanted to focus on my play, not his. It didn't matter what he did; it only mattered how I carried out my plan. Making an easy par would make him have to beat me. That kid sure looked good, though, standing there preparing his shot. He sure looked good. All these college kids with their fancy swing gurus and sports psy-chologists looked great. Don't take this the wrong way, but he had a great body. He had obviously worked with a professional trainer and had a body designed to play golf. At the same time, though, he was just a child. He hit a solid shot right of the flag. It didn't turn over as he had hoped it would, but he was 20 to 25 feet away.

"One last shot," I said to myself, walking up to my ball.

As I stood, eyeing my shot, I realized I was drenched. Perspiration? Maybe a bit, but looking up, I realized that the clouds had opened up and it had begun to drizzle.

I chose the 6 iron. A smooth 6 iron would be perfect if I hit it to the center with a little drawskee. After a few practice swings, I stepped up to the ball. There was some pulling from my shirtsleeves;

my shirt was wet, and it was sticking to my arms.

I heard a faint rumbling miles away. A storm was brewing; in the gallery, umbrellas stood at the ready. With both hands on the grip, I raised my hands over my head, sending the shaft of the club pointing straight up, hoping to unstick my shirt from my arms. Suddenly, there was a sharp crack and a blinding, brilliant light, and my body felt strangely, unbelievably warm.

The next thing I knew, I was 20 feet off the ground, looking down on the golf course. I heard a baby screaming - really wailing!

"Has that baby been crying long?" I asked myself. "Where is that baby?"

Below me, I watched as the gallery scattered. Someone was lying in the fairway. Moments later, three men approached the man on the ground, and one of them started giving him CPR. A man standing nearby was shaking his head sadly. Eventually, an ambulance came. The ambulance driver cleared the small crowd away so he and his assistant could work. Who was that, lying on the ground down there? I wondered. Then I looked closer. It was me.

eighteen

When I awoke, I didn't remember going to sleep. I didn't remember much of anything. I didn't know where I was. And strangely enough, I didn't seem to be anywhere. Everything I could see was white, and yet at the same time somehow colorless.

Then I heard a soft, fuzzy, woman's voice.

"Hello, Mark. Welcome. Today is your official day of mourning and separation. Today is your opportunity to revisit your earthly life, from the beginning to the end. You will witness your conception, revisit your childhood, review your accomplishments as an adult, on through to your demise. This should be a time of peace and comfort for you. I hope you have a nice day."

Suddenly, it hit me: I was dead. Funny, though; I sure didn't feel dead. Of course, I didn't know what dead was supposed to feel like! I will say this: nothing hurt. I wasn't even the tiniest bit stiff! A pleasant change, to say the least.

"My conception? Could we please skip that part?" I said aloud.

She was gone if she was ever there. No more voice.

I started to feel groggy, and laid back down on the white bed. My head began to spin, and then I was floating. I couldn't see or feel myself, but I knew I was floating. Looking down, I saw my parents in bed in what looked to be a motel room. They sure looked different here, 40 or 50 years do make a difference in one's appearance, I guess. My mother almost looked sexy. Jeez, what a beginning!

For the next....well, I don't know how long it was, but it was like being on an E-ticket ride at Disneyland. I watched my life unfold before my eyes. Moments of sadness; occasional moments of joy. There I was, alone in my room at one point, at odds with my father and my family in general. Another time, I was laughing at the dinner table at something my father had said that wasn't a joke. There I was again, telling my parents how much money I had made caddying at Rancho Park that day, only to have my father grimace and turn back to his television program. And finally, as my life was winding up, there was Jane. Jane. Real love, for the first time my life.

And then there I was at the U.S. Amateur. I watched intently some of the better shots I hit throughout the tournament. I was not a little impressed; I was better than I had thought. Better than I ever remembered feeling about myself. Boy, if that's not a lesson learned too late.

Then, it was the final round of the U.S. Amateur, and I was focusing on what should have been that last shot to the 17th green at Schofield Village. I sure was taking a long time to get over my ball. It looked like I was ready to win, but not quite sure if I wanted to win. I rested my hand on a club and looked at the green for what seemed an eternity. What would happen next? I didn't remember, and couldn't wait to find out.

"Come on, let's get on with it. Let's do it!" I yelled out through the void.

Finally, I stood over the ball and started to fidget with my shoulders. Then, with both hands on the grip, I stretched my arms above my head, extending the club like a lightning rod. Good move, Bozo! The bolt of lightning scored a direct hit. God hadn't needed perimeter weighting for that one; I had made

it so easy for him. Right on the sweet spot!

Then I heard the baby cry again, and looked for it in the gallery. It wasn't there. But it had to be somewhere. Where?

Suddenly, two forms appeared from the void around me. Jane, and in her arms, a crying baby. My baby.

n i n e t e e n

Next, two angelic-looking fellows appeared from out of nowhere.

"Hello, Mark," said one of them. "It's time to come with us and get assigned. Did you enjoy your day of memories?"

Before I could answer, we were walking - or at least moving, somehow - through a bank of clouds. Finally, we came to a bench in a clearing in the middle of a cloud. Four people sat on the bench. When I turned around, I saw that my escorts had disappeared as mysteriously as they had appeared.

I sat down on the bench next to another man about my age. I said hello, and he nodded at me. As time passed, several men and one woman came and went off the bench. No one said much, and no one seemed too interested in comparing notes, except the man next to me. He told me he was worried about having accidentally killed nine women. I didn't really want to hear his story; after all, how could one "accidentally" kill nine women? When the "accidental" murderer was called and left the bench, everyone gave a sigh of relief. Quickly, the mood changed to something more upbeat.

Isn't it ironic? I thought. Life seems filled with important benches. I thought of the Bentwood bench where I had sat for hours waiting for loops. I had made my best plans and taken my strongest oaths from the Bentwood caddy bench. That had been an important bench because of all I had learned there about golf, and about loneliness. And now here I was, sitting on a bench, made to wait again. What would I learn this time?

Sitting there, I thought about the life I had just seen - my life - and about my father. My father had gone off to his minimum-wage job every day, in the rain or snow if necessary, never giving what he did a second thought. He had been happy just to have a job. He never told me I would have a choice in what happened in my life. I'd had to find that out myself - but by the time I did, by the time I decided it would be "okay" to have a baby, to devote myself to golf, it turned out to be too late.

"Mark Levin," a voice said from somewhere in the cloudlike void. "Please step this way."

Following the voice to an opening in the cloud, I entered a room-like clearing in which a funny looking little man sat at a small, white desk.

"Well, well, well," he said.

"Should I even be here?" I stammered. "I mean, I'm Jewish and all."

"We're all equal in the eyes of the Committee."

"Oh," I said, unsure of what he meant.

"Well, well, well. That was an exciting tournament. Too bad you didn't get to finish," said the little man.

With his white coat, fuzzy reddish hair, and wire-rimmed glasses, he looked like that professor on the old "Superman" television programs.

"Well, it's time to get you assigned," he said, smiling at me.

"Assigned to what?" I asked.

"Well, here, everyone gets to do exactly what he wants to do, providing, of course, there is an opening. We have such a wide variety of positions available; rarely is anyone disappointed. Occasionally, some people are assigned against their will, but only because of the life they led on earth. For example, just a few moments ago a man wanted to be a care-taker at a boarding school for young ladies; it was decided this might not be a suitable assignment, given his recent earthly experiences with nine unfortunate women."

"I see," I said, even though I didn't, really.

"What would you like to do?" he asked, enthusiastically.

It didn't take me long to decide. "I want to be a touring pro, a professional golfer. Deep down inside, I've always wanted to be a professional golfer."

"Oh, jeez," he moaned" Why does everyone want to be a golf pro except former golf pros? In the last 15 years, every other Japanese guy wants to be a golf pro. Now the Committee is talking about rule changes, quotas, equal opportunity, stuff like that. This used to be a fun assignment," he said, more to himself that me.

"Listen," he said quietly" You, of all people, deserve to play golf. And you're lucky. The Committee wants you to play golf. They wanted me to persuade you to play golf."

"That won't take much persuasion," I said. "But what is this Committee?"

"The Committee decides everything around here. They won't force you to play golf if you want to be a brain surgeon, but I am informed they would strongly approve if you decided to take this assignment."

"Who is this Committee?" I asked. I was worried about this Committee. It seemed every country club had a committee run by a bunch of jerks. Why did I think it would be different up here?

"Oh, you needn't worry about the Committee if you behave yourself. However, they do decide who is worthy of the next consciousness."

"What is the next consciousness?" I asked.

"That's your reward for good deeds. You must satisfy the Committee that you are worthy."

"Worthy of what?" I wanted to know.

"How do I know? You think I would be sitting here trying to talk you into this assignment if I could just step forward to the next consciousness?" he said tersely. "I am told, however, that you can find anyone who has died before you there and be with them, if you choose, for as long as you like." He looked upward, tears coming to his eyes, and whispered, "Mildred."

"I'll give you a word of advice, pal," he said looking me straight in the eye. "Don't piss off the Committee!"

"Well, I don't mind playing golf, so I guess I won't piss off the Committee," I said.

"Good," he said.

"So what do I have to do?" I said.

"You're to be the Mulligan Man. You'll get to do over bad shots by players who are morally admirable. People who care about others, who do things to help others. People who connect with oth-ers, who love. When the Committee decides the deserving soul should get another chance, you get to go down and hit the shot."

"You'll only get that one shot to help each deserv-ing soul, though, so you'll still have to practice hard, really work on your game. I'm told the Committee has a lot of deserving souls for whom they wish you to hit shots. You'll have a lot to do."

"Why me?" I asked. "Why not Walter Hagen? Or Bobby Jones? They're both dead, right?"

"Funny you should say that," the little man said. "Once in a while, the Committee did use Walter or Bobby as Mulligan Men. But they'd have to descend from the next consciousness to do it. All that effort, just to pull off a shot for some deserving soul who had dumped it in a pond or sliced it out of bounds. Eventually, those guys told the Committee that they don't play much anymore, and that they hate like hell coming back from the next consciousness just to hit a shot, unless it's really special."

"Well, what about some more recently deceased pros?" I asked.

"Most of the players arriving here lately played mainly for the money. They don't really love the game - not like Walter and Bobby, or you. When they get up here and find they don't have to make money, most of them just want to fish.

"That leaves you," the little man continued. "Your passion for the game is well known - even legendary."

Legendary? I thought. Is it snowing up here? "Really," I said.

The little man nodded earnestly. "The Committee really wants you to fill this new spot. So what do you say? Do you want to be the Mulligan Man?"

I wondered aloud, "Why can't I just proceed to the next consciousness without being the Mulligan Man?"

"That's an easy one to answer," the little man said as his voice grew louder. "That little disappearing act you pulled last week wasn't appreciated by the Committee. Leaving Jane to fend for herself to go play golf! When the baby was just days away! You should have been there with Jane when she needed you. And because of that, you're here now. Justice? Karma? Ever heard of those things before?" He shook his head. "Guys like you really piss me off!"

How do I do it? I thought. How do I manage to piss everyone off?

"Listen," I said, "I want to do what's right. Just tell me what's the right thing to do. I really am a good guy - may be a little misguided, self-centered, egotistical, self-absorbed and selfish, but basically, I'm good. Just a few character flaws - nothing I can't work on. Please, let me show you and this Committee. I want to proceed to the next consciousness....I think."

"Good," the little man said, chuckling a bit at my cluelessness.

"So what can I do?"

"You can hit good golf shots, and help win tournaments for deserving souls."

After a second, I nodded. I would hit those shots for other people. After all, I could certainly pull off the kind of miracle shots needed at the Bentwood Invitational for some morally deserving 16 handicapper. A 7 iron from 150 yards over a pond to 20 feet would probably qualify as a miracle for the weekender who needed it to win the Secretaries flight. I started really warming to the idea. How many golfers would like to have a mulligan at some crucial time? To a professional, it could mean millions of dollars, lasting fame. How many missed 3-footers had been the difference between fame and oblivion, a stellar career and journeyman mediocrity? I laughed to myself. Maybe I'd get to the Masters, after all. Maybe the Committee would send me there, to replay an errant shot by Greg Norman.

Then I thought, hey, wait a minute - what about my shot to win the U.S. Amateur? What about my mulligan? Where was this Committee when I had needed it? Was I not a deserving soul? Why are these people I'm supposed to hit shots for more deserving than me? I was depressed at these thoughts. I had sacrificed so much, for so little in return - and I had lost Jane and the baby I would never know in the bargain. My baby would never know me, I realized. My baby would never love me, never respect me. Never would I have the chance to be there for my baby. I would be just like my father - missing from my child's life. But, unlike my father, I would not be just missing emotionally - I'd be physically absent, as well.

***

Life - life? - was suddenly strange to me. For one thing, you would never remember sleeping, but you would wake up a lot. For another, everything could be silent, and then a voice would be speaking to you from out of nowhere. For another, there was all the time in the world to daydream. It seemed it was even encouraged: taking time to reflect on what you had experienced or felt at certain points during your earthly life. It made me think a lot about my father. And somehow, I became confident I would make some kind of physical or emotional connection with him. One of the rewards of the next consciousness, I was constantly reminded, was that you could meet those who had gone before you. Meeting up with my father became my main goal. We were going to play golf together, somewhere, sometime. Even if he just walked beside me, we would connect. Even if he had never said so, I knew he loved me.

Meanwhile, I was the Mulligan Man. It was a pretty good life (life?). I got to help good people attain the happiness they deserved. I called these people I helped my NBF's, or New Best Friends, because, for a while at least, I got pretty intimately involved with their lives. The best part about the job was that I got to compete. I would go out there, and I would feel the pressure to make the shot. And I loved it. I could not imagine existence without competition.

The Committee began to appreciate my work more and more. I had plenty of time to practice, so my game got better and better. As Heaven's guest, I got to use the best practice facilities at the best clubs in the world. As I improved, I was given greater responsibility and higher-profile NBFs. Eventually, I got to go to Opens on both sides of the Atlantic, where I hit some pretty nifty shots.

Remember the one at the last Open played at Baltusrol, on the 18th hole, that seemingly went through the tree on the right side of the fairway? That was mine. Sure, it was lucky (I can't hit through trees, nor walk on water), but everyone remembers that shot. And you should have seen the shot he hit. He never even made it out of the rough behind that tree. A good guy won that tournament as a result. Too bad greed got the best of him; he started chasing equipment deals for the big bucks and then found himself in a horrible slump. He certainly learned his lesson about money.

Then there was that bunker shot I hit at the Memorial Tournament one year, also on the 18th hole. My NBF had hit out of a difficult bunker to about 20 feet above the hole, but the Committee wanted his shot much closer, and then to let the chips fall where they may. The other player, the guy with those funny pants, had hit a great bunker shot from a marginal lie to about 8 feet. No one thought I would hole out that shot, least of all me. I was high on that shot for a long time. I knew that fellow from a brief encounter on earth, and he was certainly deserving.

It's funny how things work out, sometimes. Not long ago, I got to work with the guy with the funny pants again - and this time, I got to hit a great putt to help him win the U.S. Open at Medinah. His opponent had already won the Open once before, and the

Committee had decided my NBF had paid his dues. After he three putted 15 or 16, I was sent in to lag one close so he could tap it in. His putt went 8 feet by the hole and he was really shaken by it. Now, I never prided myself as much of a putter, but even blind squirrels manage to find an acorn once in a while; I knocked that sucker in from across the green - it must have been 50 or 60 feet. Funny Pants never even cracked a smile - but he had plenty of time to smile after he had won his first Open.

And how about that shot on number 11, the second playoff hole at the Masters, a few years ago? Unfortunately, no one remembers the shot, because my NBF went on to miss a 30-inch putt to win, costing him the tournament. But it was a great shot. I hit a low percentage flop shot from a tight lie, in the dark, and put him 30 inches from the hole. He never even got his shot on the green!

And then there were all the shots that would seem to have been relatively insignificant - except to those whom I helped in the process. Guys playing five-dollar Nassaus, for instance. Very often, those shots ended up more important than shots to win the "Greater Something Open" in front of thousands of spectators, because of the way that mulligan went on to change the life of the person who'd benefited from it. Self esteem; belief in onesself. These things were far more important than trophies and checks.

Not all my shots were perfect, however. For example, in Florida, during a tour qualifier, I was sent in to hit a shot at the famous par 3 17th hole island green at Sawgrass after my NBF had hit one short into the water. It was not a terribly difficult shot, for the most part, but there was no place to bail out. It was do or die. I sent it dead at the flag, one-bouncing it on and then over the green, and into the water. I really liked this young man a lot, but I was just a little too pumped up. Because of my shot (not to mention his shot), he missed Tour school for the sixth time. I was inconsolable and sullen for a long-time after that.

It was a tough time for me. Despite the appreciation I'd gotten from the Committee, I found myself unable to take another NBF for sometime after putting that ball in the water at Sawgrass. My failure with that young golfer had brought back feelings I hadn't felt in a long time: guilt at failing Jane and my new baby by insisting on being at Schofield Village instead of in California with them on that fateful day 20 years ago.

twenty

After that, I didn't play much golf. The Committee gave me a vacation from my duties as Mulligan Man, and I quit practicing altogether. But then, after a fair amount of time had passed, I was informed that I had better start practicing again, because I'd soon have a new assignment. The Committee wasn't about to let its Mulligan Man just retire.

But try as I might, I couldn't bring myself to practice. I just no longer cared about golf. Golf had let me down too many times. No, let me rephrase that: I had used golf to let others down too many times.

Finally, the Committee gave me my comeback assignment. My next NBF was in the U.S. Amateur;

for the first time as Mulligan Man, I was to return to Schofield Village.

Immediately, I got terribly nervous. For some reason, returning to Schofield Village was immensely important to me. I was surprised by my reaction; I had played in so many huge tournaments, hit shots in so many pressure-cooker situations, that I had thought I'd never get nervous about golf again. But there I was, my heart pounding, the ants crawling down my temples at the thought of returning to Schofield Village.

I began working hard on my game, but it was too little, too late. I was going to be given a second chance at the U.S. Amateur, but because of my current jadedness about golf, I'd be rusty when I took it.

I was somewhat late getting to the course; my NBF was already out on his round. That was okay with me, though. I just wanted to be alone with my memories for a while. I sat next to the scoreboard where Mikey and I had waited to see if I would make match play, 20 years before, to the day.

The place hadn't changed much; in the air, I could sense that same magic I had felt when I played there. I had been to Opens around the world, yet had never again experienced what I felt at Schofield Village - until this moment. I thought of Mikey, waiting there silently with me on this mound of grass, just glad to be there. Suddenly, sadness overwhelmed me. Tears began to flow freely down my face and onto the grass. I thought about my father; he had missed the most satisfying accomplishment of my life. Not passing the Bar, making a lot of money, or winning a big case - playing in the U.S. Amateur. I thought of my child, of how I, like my father, would miss the most important parts of my child's life.

Suddenly, I felt a familiar, warm hand on my shoulder. Lean and strong, it was a hand I could not confuse with any other hand. Turning slowly, I saw the kind smile of my father. I remembered that smile from only one other time in my life. It was the smile I had received when I stood up to the neighborhood bully. He had been older and bigger than me, and I ended up pretty well bloodied, but I had stood up for myself. My father had understood why I'd struggled so.

"Dad?" I asked.

I reached out to touch him, to bring him closer, but already his hand was off my shoulder and he was pulling away. He still had that familiar smell: his cologne, mixed with his own natural scent. As usual, he said nothing - some things never change. But he did give me a thumbs-up and a wink. Then he disappeared. It happened so fast; there was so much I wanted to say. Eventually, I managed to convince myself it hadn't really happened, that it had been my imagination.

Jeez! What a crazy day! It was time to get going; I had work to do.

I didn't even know the name of my NBF. And quite frankly, I didn't care. After all, the assignment was always the same: one shot. I would hit the shot, then it would be on to the next one. Why get any more involved than that? The last time I had, I'd been at Sawgrass - and I didn't want to go through that kind of depression again.

The assignment was a "smooth 4 wood" to a "large green." Nothing special, apparently. My NBF had probably hooked it, or sliced it into the trees. Ho-hum, I would save the day....again.

I arrived at the 18th hole just as the players, caddies, USGA officials and crowds were walking up the fairway from the tee. From his place doing TV commentary in the network tower, I could make out the familiar voice of Mitch Coges. The scene was so much the same, yet so different. Network? What had happened to cable? This thing had gotten huge! The U.S. Amateur had truly become a popular national event. As I hovered over the 18th hole, after consciously deciding not to the visit that spot on 17 where I had died, I listened to Mitch.

"It is literally within minutes of the moment, 20 years ago, when Mark Levin was struck by lightning. Perhaps the most famous player in the history of the tournament, Levin came from nowhere and was on his way to sure victory when he was tragically struck down on 17."

Nice, nice. I got goosebumps as Mitch went on to talk about the things my competitors from that U.S. Amateur had said about me over the years. Good things. Very good things.

Realizing that I needed to get ready for my shot, I tried to tune Mitch out. While swinging two irons to loosen up, I watched the action below. There, my NBF was looking into the fairway bunker, staring at his ball. Totally psyched out, apparently.

To review, this hole was 437 yards long, a dogleg right with a limited landing area. What made the landing area limited were the trees guarding the inside and outside of the elbow of the dogleg. My NBF must have caught the right tree and ended up in the right fairway bunker. I knew from what the Committee had told me that he was tied going into this hole, so from here he needed a miracle shot just to give himself a chance to win for a playoff. His opponent was in the fairway with a straightforward shot to the green. Winning at this point could not be the primary focus.

"Smooth 4 wood to large green," my wings! Jeez! They might as well have covered the green with windmills and castles! This just wasn't fair; it was an impossible assignment. I looked at my NBF, looking down at his ball and shaking his head. Poor guy. I wondered who he was.

Behind me, Mitch continued his commentary. "Mark Levin looks to be considering his next shot carefully. He might have any of a thousand thoughts I can think of going through his mind right about now."

Mark who? What was Mitch saying?

"Twenty years ago today, Mark's father also faced a similarly difficult shot. a shot that could to win the U. S. Amateur, which would have placed him in the history books of the USGA and thrust upon him golfdom immortality."

Oh, my God. Mark Levin. My son. Here, with me. The ants began to crawl down my neck.

"Instead, a cult was born. The name Mark Levin will always be synonymous with dreams that come true. Not because he won the U.S. Amateur; he did not. Not because he hit a most brilliant shot when summoned to do so; he was struck down before he had that chance. And not because his was such a celebrated golfing career; in fact, it had hardly begun. Rather, it is because Mark Levin came from nowhere and earned himself a chance to put himself in the record books. Something every golfer can relate to. It is tragic that he was so abruptly deprived of his chance for success."

twenty one

Finally, it was now or never. There was no putting it off any further. First I had to watch my son hit his version of the shot out of the bunker. He was away, and would go first. Deliberately, he tried to put the shot together. First he had an iron; then, finally, he decided on a fairway wood. I heard Mitch up in the tower tell everyone how I had been this great fairway wood player out of bunkers, and now my son was about to try to hit one of those same shots. Where do these guys get some of the crap they say on television? I thought. I was no more known for hitting fairway bunker shots than the man in the moon. I did have a good bunker game around the green, but I was hardly another Gary Player. In the end, the truth was that I was not known for my golf game, but for being in the wrong place at the wrong time.

As my son deliberated, I found myself staring at Jane. She was unbelievably beautiful, even after 20 years. A bit older maybe, but still fresh and radiant. A sense of loss covered me immediately; I could hardly breathe because of it.

Soon, my son stood over his ball. He got into the bunker and wasted no time getting set and pulling the trigger. His shot was a high cut toward the left side of the green. He had picked it very clean, maybe even a little thin. It looked great; it was heading toward the flag, moving left to right. He didn't need me, after all, I thought to myself - until it plugged in the front bunker. Ugh! What a miserable lie. And now it was time for me to go to work. To help my son. I got scared and excited, all at the same time.

While I descended to the fairway, I wondered what "little" Mark had done to deserve this second chance, this mulligan. What made him different, more deserving, from what I had been? I quickly decided that it really didn't matter. All I cared about was how proud I was of my son, for playing well enough to get here, and for being the kind of person who deserves a mulligan.

Down on the fairway, I studied Jane. Her face had dropped. For the second time in her life, it seemed, her man was going to have the chance to achieve his dream, only to fall sadly short. It was difficult for me to watch the light go out in her eyes. I wanted to reach out to her, to hold her close. I wanted to protect her. Suddenly, I realized that this mulligan was not just for my son. It was for Jane. And if I did well, then maybe it would be for me, too.

Then I looked over at my son. His lips were

pursed in a wry smile to show his disappointment. I had never seen him do this, but I knew exactly what it meant - because I would have done the same thing in the same circumstance. Imagine: Jane living with my son and watching him do all the things I did, watching him make all the same silly faces and gestures. Wearing a part of his father in a way he would never know or recognize.

I couldn't stand the hurt! All I wanted to do was get in there and relieve the disappointment I felt. Maybe this was really my mulligan on life, the second chance to make things right. Why hadn't I prepared better? I was so mad, I could've killed myself - if that had been at all possible.

I suddenly felt very selfish. I had not practiced sufficiently to prepare for this moment. I realized that life should always be filled with preparation, because you never knew what would be ahead of you. Golf is a game where how you feel means more than anything else, and because I hadn't prepared, I wasn't feeling great right about now. Ironically, I had always felt confident that I could save the day for people with whom I had no connection, and now I felt unsure whether I had enough left to help my son when he needed it most - when we needed it most.

As I stepped into the fairway bunker, I thought about that putt on the 18th green to qualify for my first Amateur. I can do this, I said to myself. I can do this. Perspiration gathered on my forehead and dripped into my eyes, and I got out of the bunker to regroup and wipe my face. Looking up at the sky, I noticed the clouds darkening; rain was coming. How fitting, I thought. Just like my last shot at Schofield.

I stepped back in the bunker, and I glanced at the gallery. There he was again - my father. Standing in the gallery, his arms folded in his usual manner. Winking, he gave me the thumbs-up sign.

At that moment, I may have been the happiest man in heaven. My father had come to see the most important shot I would ever hit! I was not alone! Suddenly confident again, I turned back to my shot. It was time to do it - now.

Taking out a metal wood, I settled down to prepare for the shot. The sand was firm; I had a pretty good lie. Still, I would rather have been hitting a pitching wedge from 115 yards than a 4 wood out of a fairway bunker for my son's mulligan.

Finally, I got set. I felt good over the ball and put a good swing on it, with solid contact. The ball headed left of the green, then started to cut back nicely. This was fun. This was as good as life - death? - could be. I admired my handiwork, just wanting the ball to stay in flight forever. This was a shot I would never forget - a shot a lot of people would never forget.

As the ball homed in on the flag, I thought of how fitting it would be to hole out from the fairway bunker, for my son, and in the presence of my father. This looked to be a shot for the ages - maybe right up there with Gene Sarazen's double eagle on the 15th hole at the Masters. Landing right in front of the flag, the ball started to roll toward the hole. We couldn't see it from the fairway, but we all knew it would be close. The gallery roared, but we still couldn't tell where the ball was. The on-course commentator following us knew where it was, from the audio feed coming through his headphones, but decided to stay neutral and just shrugged his shoulders when Mark looked his way. Mark and Jane's spirits were soaring, and I wanted these same spirits to wrap around me, to engulf me.

I couldn't get enough of the intoxicating vibes they were sending out.

Then I realized I had completely forgotten about Mark's opponent. I had to calm down, to get a grip! The opponent, who had a five or six iron in his hand, complimented Mark and then began his own pre-shot routine. A very competent player (not as competent as my son, though), he put a good swing on a ball that found its way to the right side of the flag, about 20 feet. We couldn't tell if it was hole-high, but it looked pretty good from where we were. "Nice shot," Mark said politely. That's my boy! I thought.

Needless to say, this was not over yet for my son. Often, the Committee would give someone a mulligan that was not capitalized upon; I had hit many shots that had won the battle but not the war. So, of course, I wondered if that would be the case here.

The Committee works in strange ways, as I knew all too well by then.

When we got to the 18th green, only one ball was on the carpet, about 15 to 20 feet right of the hole. And it wasn't Mark's ball. How strange; we weren't prepared for what had happened. Apparently, his ball - our ball - had hit on the back tier, trying to check, but scooted over the green into the back bunker. "Stunned" is a good word for the way we all felt, standing there in awkward silence.

All I wanted to do next was plead with the Committee to give me another chance. "Let me hit Mark's bunker shot, pleeeeeease?" I couldn't believe it - my great shot had turned out to be another disaster!

Suddenly, I felt that warm, familiar hand on my shoulder again. It was my dad. "He can hit this shot," he said. "This is your mulligan, son."

My mulligan? What did he mean by that? I tried to ask, but before I could, my dad had disappeared again. But strangely, I was no longer worried. My father's voice was so reassuring, so comforting to me. Did he mean that he was going to be my backup?

Meanwhile, my son was preparing to take his next shot. Even though he was off the green, his ball was inside the ball on the green, so he would get to watch his opponent putt. Nearby him, Jane had her hands in her mouth; apparently, she had given up caddying for the time being. Not that I'm judging her, or anything; I was probably as much of a basket case as she was.

After what seemed to be an eternity, the putt was finally struck. My heart was in my mouth as I watched the ball go into, then out of, the hole. I col-

lapsed onto Jane - or more accurately, through Jane. I couldn't touch her even if I tried. As I stood up and composed myself, Mark's opponent tapped in for 4.

Mark's bunker shot was slightly downhill. He had a good lie - so good that putting the ball through the bunker was an option. The green was also running downhill and away from him. Between the ball and the hole were 2 feet of sand, 4 feet of collar, plus maybe 11 feet of green. He only needed to get it close to go to the next tee for a sudden-death play-off. He didn't need to be a hero just yet.

Finally, Mark decided upon the putter. To me this was the high percentage shot to get it within 5 feet, to give himself a chance at par. He's got brains just like his dad, I thought, not too modestly. But then he had the pin pulled. Maybe he doesn't have his dad's brains, I thought questioning his strategy. Then, stepping into the bunker, Mark choked up on his putter and made several practice strokes. Thunder rumbled in the distance, and Mark stepped away from his shot to look at the ominous sky. Eerie, how similar this day was to the day on which I had died. My son, I was sure, was thinking the same thing. I only prayed he was not scared. Readying himself again, he hit his putt. As soon as he hit it, I thought that he had killed it.

"Bite!" I yelled, even though no one could hear me.

Hitting the lip of the bunker, the ball jumped up in the air.

"Go!" I yelled as the ball trickled through the froghair on its way to the green. "Go! Go!"

The ball made its way onto the green, and kept rolling, right at the hole. Finally, it stopped, looking in. Mark froze. Jane froze. The gallery froze. Time seemed to stop. Only one man was moving in the gallery. Looking over, I saw that it was my dad, smiling, his arms folded as he rocked back on his heels. Just then, a flash of lightning appeared on the next fairway and the loudest crashing noise I've ever heard filled the air. And dutifully, the ball dropped in the hole.

EPILOGUE

After winning the U.S. Amateur and going on to law school, Mark Levin became a prominent lawyer. Just like his father. But unlike his father, he loves to practice law - sports law.

Jane finally met a man she could love, the first since the tragic death of her husband more than 20 years before. Her new husband plays tennis. As for me, I finally made it to the next consciousness. I do, however, still spend some of my time as the Mulligan Man. I watch my son at work and in his weekend foursome at his club. Even though sometimes I'd like to, I don't interfere with his life. No more mulligans - he's doing just fine.

On Friday afternoons, I play with my dad. Soon, I even hope to beat him.